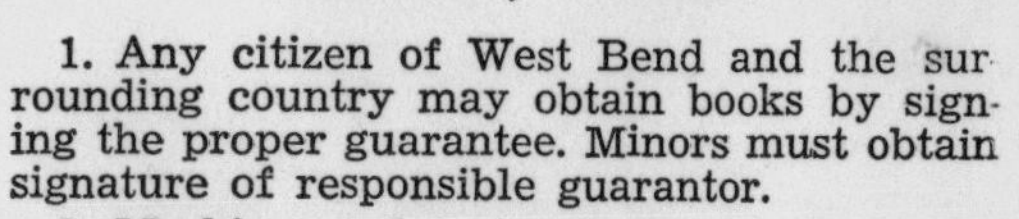

TALES OF CHRISTMAS FROM NEAR AND FAR

BOOKS BY HERBERT H. WERNECKE
Published by The Westminster Press®

Tales of Christmas from Near and Far
Celebrating Christmas Around the World
Christmas Stories from Many Lands
Christmas Customs Around the World
Christmas Songs and Their Stories

TALES *of* CHRISTMAS *from* NEAR *and* FAR

Edited by
Herbert H. Wernecke

Philadelphia
THE WESTMINSTER PRESS

LIBRARY OF CONGRESS CATALOG CARD NO. 63-10832

PUBLISHED BY THE WESTMINSTER PRESS ®

PHILADELPHIA 7, PENNSYLVANIA

PRINTED IN THE UNITED STATES OF AMERICA

Contents

Contents

Contents

Foreword

THIS FIFTH VOLUME in the "Christmas Around the World" series seeks to continue and to enlarge the influence that its predecessors have had in helping to release the flood of goodwill among men that the Christmas season inevitably brings every year we are privileged to observe it.

The very word "Christmas" brings joy to children as they look forward for weeks, even months, to its approach with its surprises. Adults likewise find its appeal irresistible, so that the spirit of Tiny Tim frequently transforms a quarrelsome Scrooge. Millions find an upsurge of happiness when they watch the children play with new toys, and jointly children and adults rejoice in family fun and feasting. This is good and can mean much for many whose lives are drab and dull, or even hard and bitter.

TALES OF CHRISTMAS FROM NEAR AND FAR seeks to transform drab and dull lives by encouraging more people to join the fellowship of Christmas around the world. Its aim is to bring together neighbors and friends in church, school, and community gatherings to absorb and express the spirit that pervades the observance of this sacred and seasonal festival.

Though basically Christmas will always be a religious, even a Christian, festival, it has at the same time engendered a spirit of goodwill throughout the world through intercommunication of many kinds; so that non-Christian countries and peoples join in its spirit and observance, inspiring "peace on earth, goodwill to men."

Once more, Mrs. Milton Lutz deserves special thanks for typing the greater part of the manuscript.

H. H. W.

Acknowledgments

THOUGH THE MATERIALS included in this volume were gathered over a period of years and in several cases from out-of-the-way places, practically all the authors and publishers concerned could be located. If any errors have crept in as to crediting copyrighted material, kindly notify the editor, and corrections will be made.

Special acknowledgment is made and appreciation expressed to the following:

Alfred A. Knopf, Inc., for "Song from Heaven," from *Silent Night*, by Hertha Pauli, copyright 1943 by Alfred A. Knopf, Inc. Also for "Marushka's Christmas Joys," from *Happy Times in Czechoslovakia*, by Libushka Bartusek, copyright 1940. Both selections are used by permission of the publisher.

The American Girl, for "Christmas at Thunder Gap," by Katherine O. Wright.

Augsburg Publishing House, for the following materials reprinted from *Christmas: An American Annual of Christmas Literature and Art:* "Annaliese's Christmas Wish," by Gertrude Doederlein, Vol. 24 (1954), pp. 65–67; "Jenny Lind's Yuletide," by Burnette Thompson, Vol. 17 (1947), pp. 53–60; "A Christmas Letter," by Gertrude Hanson, Vol. 16 (1946), pp. 57–64; "One of the Least Ones," by Edna and Howard Hong, Vol. 14 (1944), pp. 27–32; "On Christmas Day," by Margaret W. Eggleston, Vol. 5 (1935), pp. 63 ff.; "For the Children from Possum Run," by Grace Noll Crowell, Vol. 10 (1940), pp. 68–71; "The Christmas Candle," by Charles Stryker Ingerman, Vol. 15 (1945), pp. 45 ff.; "A Day of Work and No Cheer" ("A Puritan Christmas"), by Lois Lenski, Vol. 11 (1941), pp. 37–43; "Christmas on Tinicum" ("A Swedish Christmas on the Delaware"), by Elsie Singmaster, Vol. 6 (1936), pp. 41–43.

Christian Publications, Inc., for "God's Christmas Gift to Rare Coral," from *More Rainbow Stories*, by Stella M. Rudy (1946), pp. 92–97. Used by permission of Christian Publications, Inc., Harrisburg, Pennsylvania.

Doubleday & Co., Inc., for "Christmas in a French-Canadian Home," from *Petite Suzanne*, by Marguerite de Angeli, pp. 168–186.

Friendship Press, for "Come to Christmas," by Jessie Eleanor Moore, and "The Lights of Christmas," by Elizabeth Allstrom, from *Missionary Stories to Play and Tell*, edited by Nina Millen, pp. 40–45.

Harper & Row, Publishers, Inc., for "The Christmas Angel," "An Indian's Christmas Gift," and "The Smiling Lady," from *The Red Stocking and Other Christmas Stories*, by Margaret W. Eggleston. Copyright by Harper & Row, Publishers, Inc. Also "The Little Clockmaker," by Ruth Sawyer, from her book *This Way to Christmas*, copyright 1916 by Harper & Row, Publishers, Inc.

The Macmillan Company, for "Maminka's Children's Christmas Dreams and Joys," from *Maminka's Children*, by Elizabeth Orton Jones, pp. 91–107. Copyright 1940 by The Macmillan Company and used with their permission. Also, for "Christmas Eve in the Tyrolean Alps," by Ludwig Bemelmans, from *Told Under the Christmas Tree*, copyright 1950. Used by permission of the Association for Childhood Education International.

David McKay Company, Inc., for "Christmas in the Philippines," from *Pedro's Coconut Skates*, by Esther Wood.

Etta W. Schlichter, for "The Pelaski Children's Christmas," from *Christmas Stories Told by Aunt Theresa* (The Moody Press, 1947), pp. 47–51.

Ella Maie Seyfert, for "An Amish Christmas," from *The Little Amish Schoolhouse* (1939), pp. 74–96.

The United Church Board for World Ministries, Division of World Service, for "Ciro's Bigger World," by Alice Geer

Kelsey. (Based on a letter from Hulda Stettler, social worker for the Congregational Christian Service Committee in Naples, Italy.)

The Viking Press, for "The Holy Lake," by Ruth Sawyer, from *The Long Christmas*, by Ruth Sawyer. Copyright 1941 by Ruth Sawyer. Reprinted by permission of The Viking Press, Inc.

Whiteside, Inc., and William Morrow & Co., Inc., for "A Carol for Katrusia," by Annie B. Kerr, from *So Gracious Is the Time* (1938).

AUSTRIA

Christmas Eve in the Tyrolean Alps

LUDWIG BEMELMANS

"CHRISTMAS EVE," thought Hansi, "should start with the evening. There should be no day on that day at all."

Certainly it was the biggest day in the year and the longest to wait around in.

He was sent from the house on errands as soon as he came in. Packages wandered around. One room was locked and even the keyhole stuffed so one could see nothing.

The children weren't hungry, though there were the most wonderful things on the table.

"Hansi, nothing is going to happen until this plate is empty. Lieserl, stop wiggling on that chair." Uncle Herman finally looked at his watch and got up. Soon a little silver bell rang, and sparkling across the hall stood the Christmas tree. It turned slowly to music, as glass angels, cookies, and burning candles rode around.

The best skis in the whole world are made of Norwegian spruce, with long, tapered ends. Such a pair stood beside the tree—new and with a binding like that the champion jumpers use. Next to them was a skiing cap with a long tassel. Aunt Amalie had knitted it for Hansi. The skis, of course, were from his mother. Uncle Herman had given Hansi a skiing jacket, bright red and warm, so that one could get lost and yet stay warm and easily be found in the white snow.

Lieserl had a doll carriage, with a big doll dressed like a peasant girl on Sunday. This doll could go to sleep, and even said "Mamma" when she was pinched.

"Yes, Lieserl, I see," said Hansi, and looked at his skis again.

Hansi had barely slipped into the skis to try them on, and put the stocking cap on his head, when singing was heard outside the house.

"Here they are," said Uncle Herman. Everybody tiptoed to the door, and quietly it swung open.

Three kings stood majestically in the starry night and sang in verses. They told how they had come from the sands of the desert and were passing this house on the way to visit the *Christ Kinderl,* to offer him their precious gifts. Long, heavy robes of scarlet flowed off them into the snow. Over their serious, devout faces shone tall crowns of pure gold. Their hands were hidden in the deep folds of the scarlet sleeves, and one of them held a silver lance on which shone the star that had guided the kings from the East past this house.

After they had finished their song, Uncle Herman invited them to enter his home. He did so, singing a verse to which they answered with singing and came in.

Aunt Amalie had brought three cups of hot chocolate and a big plate of lebkuchen. The kings seemed to be very hungry indeed after the hard trip from the hot desert and over the cold mountains. Each took three lebkuchen as they sat down, falling over the plate in their hurry to reach it. One lebkuchen was left, and as one of the kings tried to reach for it, the biggest one hit him on the fingers with the silver lance to which was attached the morning star, which broke off and fell into the chocolate. Uncle Herman seemed to know these kings very well. He took the lances away from them so they would not hurt each other any more.

Lieserl sat down next to the smallest king, who was black, and looked at him very closely. Then she wet her finger and rubbed his nose. The king started to cry, and his nose turned white.

"I knew it all the time," said Lieserl. "It's Frau Kofler's little boy Peterl."

Now Hansi came to the table and he could see that the king, outside of a black face, had only black fingernails. His hands were white—almost white. They were boys from the village.

The beautiful stars and crowns were made with gold and silver paper pasted over them, and the little king was blackened with burnt cork.

They had to sing at three more houses, they said. Aunt Amalie brought two more lebkuchen, so each could eat another, and Uncle Herman repaired the little king's pale nose with stove blacking. They gave thanks with a little verse for the shelter and food and bowed and walked back into the night. The cold light of the moon gave them back their lost majesty. As they left, everyone was serious and quiet. Their stars and crowns had turned again to purest beaten gold.

The evening passed as quickly as the day had been slow in going. Soon it was time to go to midnight services.

This was one of three days in the year when Uncle Herman stood in front of a mirror. He buttoned his tunic and pinned his medals on according to regulation, "six fingers down from the seam of the collar, three fingers over from the second button—right over the heart." Belt and saber were adjusted carefully. Uncle Herman breathed on the buckle and polished it with his sleeve.

Aunt Amalie said: "Why don't you ask for a piece of cloth? It's a shame—the nice new uniform."

The feathers on the green huntsman's hat were straightened out, the white gloves put on.

The children looked up in awe at their new uncle, who looked like a picture of his old emperor.

Aunt Amalie had her best dress on, with a wide silk shawl around her shoulders, and silver lacing from which jingled talers as she walked.

Hansi and Lieserl sat around like pictures painted on the wall. They had been ready for an hour, and held the little lanterns that were used to light the way down the path.

Aunt Amalie put some things on the table for a small supper when they came back.

The night helped to make Christmas. All the stars were out. The windows of the mountain church shone out into the blue night from the valley, and from high up, little rows of lights came toward the church. People carried them. They shone up into happy, quiet faces. Silent night, holy night—only the bells of the churches rang from near and from the far white fields.

They scraped the snow from their shoes and entered the church. It smelled like a cool forest at noontime when the sun shines through the tall pines. Pines stood in rows along the walls, reaching almost to the tower. Candles flickered everywhere.

Hansi walked up the creaky stairway that led through the tower and opened into the choir. A big oil lamp hung over the organ that was built a century ago. In front of it sat the village schoolmaster. He gave Hansi notes and nodded to the place where he was to stand with other boys. Behind him a man was tuning two large copper kettledrums. He bent his ear close to them and struck them with a softly padded hammer. It was a lovely warm sound that made Hansi feel hollow inside.

Post Seppl was up here with a trumpet, and there were the players of two more instruments—a flute and a fiddle.

In front of the organ, above the schoolmaster's head, was a little mirror. In this the teacher watched the services. He could tell when to play, and he kept the time by nodding his head.

The church below was filled to the doors with kindly people who thanked God for their beautiful mountains and asked no more of him than that he keep them as he had all the years of their plain, good lives.

The old teacher lifted his eyes and asked, in addition, for his help in repairing this poor tired organ. Not only were many important sounds missing—there were others that did not make melodies, and of the two wooden angels that flew to the left and the right of it, one needed his robe painted and the other had lost a wing.

After services Uncle Herman waited below with Aunt Amalie and Lieserl for Hansi. They went home together as they had come, with other little lights that wandered from the church to the houses on the mountain.

The Holy Lake

RUTH SAWYER

IT LIES high up in the Dolomites in a straight line between Innsbruck and Verona. The water is clear; it carries on its cold blue surface the impression of crystal glass, an impression that if you should look through it, you could see something. And you would, if the day were clear and still. If you should stand on one of those high places surmounting the lake, you would see, far down, a drowned village lying peacefully there in what was once a green valley.

Long ago there were silver mines about the village. Those who came to work them grew rich. It was fabulous how rich they grew. They put up houses far finer than any other village could boast of. They built a large church—far too large to hold the number of people in the village, with far too towering a steeple to keep guardianship over the shrunken souls that dwelt beneath it. For the people of the village lived by the vast tons of silver they mined; they lived for the silver. They threw away everything made of the baser metals and replaced these with silver. They ate from silver dishes; they drank from silver mugs; they burned their candles in silver sticks; they wore silver buttons and silver buckles. Their salutations were no longer: "Good day," or "God keep you," but "God give you more silver." It was only in this greeting that God got into their lives at all.

And yet it seemed as if God must have heard their daily greeting, and was pleased by it. For no sooner did one vein of silver in a mine run out than a new vein was discovered. There seemed no end to the wealth of the mountains. And at night, of a full, high moon, the villagers would point to one of the many waterfalls that came cascading down the sides of the mountains, fed abundantly by the melting glaciers and snows, and say, "See—even our brooks run silver." And this seemed true.

They became proud and scornful, the people of the village, proud and scornful of the people of other villages, of all their neighbors in the Dolomites. It was as if the world around them had no importance; as if nothing were good enough that they had not bought with their silver or made out of it.

Now, pride and scorn are poor bedfellows. They will turn a good man into an empty-headed fool. If there is no longer need of earning daily bread, no longer need of counting the busy hours of the day that life might be wise and diligent, then the empty-headed fool becomes a man both vicious and greedy—a baser metal himself, and good for little but scrapping.

They became great eaters in the village, eaters of fine foods brought over the mountain on donkeyback and in lumbering carts. They became great drinkers. Not content with the wine from neighboring vineyards, they must have casks of the best, brought from wherever the world made it. So they ate much and drank much and were exceedingly merry, or thought they were. Every day became a holiday and a feast day; and when a real holiday came they had to whip it up into a time of wild orgy, that they might put upon it the extra importance it should have. Saints' days, holy days, lost all meaning for them beyond the table, the wine cask, the gaming, and the dancing. Although they paid a priest well to keep the Sabbath for them, they kept little of it for themselves.

Many years went by. Sons born to drinking fathers became good drinkers in their turn; daughters born to vain, light-minded mothers became flirts and wantons. Generations can build a village or blight it. And this one, in its green valley, became blighted.

Now, of all the seasons of the year which offered the greatest number of days for celebration and the most abundant excuse for wanton gaiety the best was the Christmas season. In the streets as well as the houses the people caroused. They brought their wine casks in sleighs into the market square; they poured red wine not only down their own throats but down the throats of their servants, their horses, and even their game cockerels. The air was filled with raucous laughter, vulgar joking, ribald singing. Night became day, and day night; and so the Eve of Christmas came.

Standing above the village, looking down on it, had you been there and so minded, you would have seen a picture that could well have been painted upon a card. Just such a village with the church spire and cross above it; snow binding hill and meadow together, making heavy the spruce and fir. And finally, as night fell, the snow coming down in large and lazy flakes, like powdered mica that you sprinkle on the card to make it seem truly Christmas. Everything looked soft and glinting, and showing through it were the copper lights of candles at the windows. If I had sent the card to you, you would have said: "What a lovely card! What a joyous and peaceful Christmas village." That is what you would have said.

At nightfall, with the snow, there came a young boy from the south. Rough clothes he wore, poorly clad, without cap, without stout mountain boots. His lips were blue with cold, his fingers pinched, his jacket tight about him. His eyes, blue as strawflowers, looked hollowed and hungry from under his heavy thatch of corn-colored hair. He came laggardly down the last of the trails, and reaching the village street, he began at the farthest end to knock at every door.

Knock-knock-knock!

"What do you want?"

"Something to stay my hunger, a place to warm my heart."

"We are feasting tonight. We have no room for a stranger."

"I have come far. My home lies beyond the mountain, over the sea."

"Then go back to it!"

Knock-knock-knock!

"What do you want?"

"Something to stay my hunger, a place to warm my heart."

"We are feasting tonight. We have no room for a stranger."

"I have come far. My home lies beyond the mountains, over the sea."

"Then go back to it!"

Knock-knock-knock!

Down the long length of the street on one side, back the long length on the other, the knocking went on. Some did not open the door at all. Some opened but to slam it again when the visitor was seen to be poor and a stranger.

Knock-knock-knock! It sounded louder as the night grew darker. It sounded above the shouting, the laughter, the singing. It came at last to fill the valley, echoing now from this side, now from that. It filled the very dome of heaven, until it might have been a knocking at heaven's door.

As the eve waxed into night, as the night waxed toward the coming Christmas Day, the swelling sound of the knocking was borne in upon the men and women, even upon the children tossing restlessly in their cots. They cried out in their sleep in a kind of fear, so that the peasant maids who tended them had to hush and bid them sleep again, promising again and again that nothing was amiss.

"What is it that we hear?" they asked.

"It is someone knocking at a door."

"Why isn't he let in? Why isn't he let in?"

"That is not our business. Go to sleep."

Their elders grew restless, likewise. A cup, filled anew with red wine, would be half lifted to the lips, then stayed while the drinker would listen for the knocking, which seemed no longer to come upon a door but rather upon his heart. Knock-knock-knock! Lovers held back the very words of love upon their lips to listen; then, shuddering, turned to their lovemaking again with faint hearts. Those who danced, those who threw dice, those who went back to the platters and goblets, paused oftener and oftener, until their half-befuddled minds could no longer keep off the sound that waxed and waned along the street, waxed and waned and waxed again.

"Curse you—throw the dice! Stop listening to that infernal knocking."

"The wine's grown sour; bring fresh."

"The lights are dim; fetch more candles."

"Your love sounds hollow."

"Your words have grown cold."

"The music's out of tune."

"This is no pavane—why do your feet stumble?"

"Send someone abroad to stop that cursed knocking."

Servants were dispatched at last. They bore heavy cudgels to enforce their command that the boy must stop his knocking and leave the village. But although they searched the street, looked well into each shadowed doorway and bystreet, they found the village deserted save for one of their own people, going his drunken way. They returned to their masters and reported. Spirits rose. "He's gone, good riddance!" they shouted.

"Fill up the goblets!"

"I'll lay you thirty pieces of silver on the next throw of the dice."

But the boy—where was he? Finding every door in the village shut to him, he climbed to the nearest peasant hut and knocked there. An old grandmother came to the door, rubbing her hands. She saw the lonely child, the poor covering on his body, the hunger in his eyes, and the deep-rooted weariness in the droop of his young body.

"Poor lad, poor lad, come in." She drew him to the fire, pulling out a stool, pushing him down, that he might be closer to the warmth. "Hast eaten?" And not waiting for an answer, she went for a bowl, to fill it with the hot broth that stood on the hearth. She cut the thick bread for him, and brought some goat's cheese. "It is thine, poor fare as it is. Nay, speak not until thou art fed."

She sat and watched him eat, clucking over every mouthful as one clucks to a young bird that eats out of one's hand. She twice filled the bowl with broth. And then, seeing the raggedness of his garments, she took off the jacket and with thread and needle and woolen patches she mended it, talking the while.

"Thou art alone. Hast thou come far? Hast thou no parents?"

"I have thee, Grandmother," said the boy.

"Surely, and I have thee. That is good. To be alone, to have one's kin gone, is a lonesome thing on Christmas Eve."

"Thou rememberest, then, what night it is?"

"Surely. It is a poor keeping we make of it in these parts. Soon will come the Midnight Mass, and I shall go. But it will be the same as other years—a sodden, drunken crowd that falls asleep at their worship, that does not even know when the name of the blessed Christ and his mother Mary are spoken. They cannot even cross themselves, they are so far gone with wine."

"I know," said the boy. "I know."

"Let us go to the church together. There will then be two worshipers who can pray with loving hearts."

"We stay here, Grandmother. We do not go."

The old woman looked at him, wondering. The light of the fire played about his golden hair, giving it a strange and spreading light. There was no more hunger in his eyes; but looking deep within them, she saw austerity. They were no longer the eyes of the youth but the everlasting eyes of Eternal Judgment.

"Who art thou, lad?" asked the old woman.

"One thou hast always known well, Grandmother."

And at that moment the bells from below rang out their summons to the Christmas Mass. "I have never missed going," sighed the old woman. "The bells on this Eve have made the pleasantest sound for me of all the year. They bring back to me the children, Gordo and Vinella, and the grandchildren, Maria, Lazar, and Rosa." She went to her window and looked down upon the church.

The boy stood beside her. "Come away from the window, Grandmother. If thou wilt come, I give thee my promise thou shalt hear the bells ringing at Christmas Eve so long as thou livest and after. Come away. For what thou shalt presently see below is a sight too sad for thine eyes."

Already the bells had brought people tumbling out of their doors, tumbling and staggering, shouting and making all manner of loud, raucous sounds. "They should come quietly and reverently," mumbled the old woman.

"They will be quiet soon enough—let them shout now."

The old woman turned, her eyes grown suddenly wide with fear. "Who art thou?" she asked again. "Why will the wicked ones soon be quiet? What is to happen this night?"

"Be not afraid, Grandmother. There is a saying known to thee, no doubt: 'Yea, the light of the wicked shall be put out, and the spark of his fire shall not shine.' Come away!"

He drew her tenderly to the hearth, put fresh fagots on the fire, sat her in her chair, took the stool and sat at her feet, laid her hands peacefully upon her lap, crossing them with his own. And then he talked to her of his own mother, of their simple life at home, of his brothers and one sister. She saw, in what he told, her own life taking form as it had been, and felt again how good it had been, these things of living, of homely service, of preparing food, of hushing children, of making garments, of keeping a house tidy and pleasant. And while he talked, bringing the years home to her, she nodded and at last slept.

The sun was over all when she awoke Christmas morning. She looked to find the boy, but he had gone. Yet wood stood heaped plentifully upon the hearth, and food stood in abundance upon the shelves. The rosebush at her window, which had borne only green leaves since summer, was now in full bloom.

"He is gone, and I did not learn his name," she mumbled to herself regretfully, going to the window to wonder and feel and smell the beauty of the roses. Their fragrance almost overpowered her; dizzily she looked up and out. Snow bound together the mountains and the meadows, but below—below where, since she was born, the village had stood, there was no village! A lake covered the valley, filled it with crystal-blue water, already turning to brittle ice.

" 'Yea, the light of the wicked shall be put out, and the spark of his fire shall not shine.' " She repeated the words slowly, as if saying them after him who had first said them. She spoke in awe: "I did not need to ask his name," she said.

And so the lake stands—the Holy Lake, it is called. In summer many come to see the village lying there under its clear waters. And on Christmas Eve those who pass, even far away, can still hear the ringing of the church bells, ringing the summons to the Christmas Midnight Mass. As the promise was made, so has the promise been kept.

Song from Heaven

HERTHA PAULI

ON THE 24TH of December, 1818, in Hallein, an age-old village in the Austrian Alps, Father Joseph Mohr sat alone in his study, reading the Bible. All through the valley the children were filled with excitement, for it was Holy Eve, and they could stay up for Midnight Mass. On their way down the open, frozen trails they carried rushlights, so that from the village the valley looked like a huge Christmas tree with a hundred moving candles.

The young priest had no eyes for the valley that was so festively lighted. With open Bible, he sat at his oaken study table working on a sermon for the midnight service. He read again the story of the shepherds in the fields to whom the angel came and said: "Unto you is born this day in the City of David a Saviour . . ."

Just as Father Mohr read this passage a knock sounded at his door. He admitted a peasant woman wrapped in a coarse shawl, who told him of a child born earlier that day to a poor charcoal maker's wife living on one of the highest alps in his parish. The parents had sent her to ask the priest to come and bless the infant, that it might live and prosper.

Father Mohr was strangely moved on his visit to the poorly lighted ramshackle hut where the young mother lay on the crude bed smiling happily, with her baby asleep in her arms. The scene certainly did not resemble the manger in the City of David, yet the last words he had read in his Bible suddenly seemed to be addressed to him. When he returned to the valley, he saw that the dark slopes were alight with the torches of the mountaineers on their way to church, and from all the villages far and near, bells began to ring.

To Father Mohr a true Christmas miracle had come to pass. Sitting in his study after the midnight service, he tried to put down on paper what had happened to him. The words kept turning into verse, and when dawn broke, Father Mohr had written a poem. And on Christmas Day his friend, Franz Xavier Gruber, music teacher in the village school, composed music to fit the verses.

Village children heard the priest and the teacher singing. The church organ was out of order, so the pair were using what they had—two voices and a guitar, which Franz Gruber played. "The Lord can hear us without an organ," Gruber said.

They did not know that this anniversary of Christ's birthday was also the birthday of a great Christmas hymn that would be known in all lands where there is a Christmas, and that four little children would one day start it on its way to fame.

Of all the youngsters in the Zillertal valley in the Austrian Tyrol, the ones with the most beautiful voices were the four Strasser children, Caroline, Joseph, Andreas, and little Amalie, who was called Maly, and was so young that she couldn't pronounce the words correctly.

"Those Strassers," the townspeople used to say, "sing just like the nightingales."

Like the nightingales too, every spring the four children traveled northward to Leipzig, in the kingdom of Saxony, the site of the great annual Trade Fair. For their parents were glove makers, and it was the children's chore to display and sell the soft chamois gloves that were sought far and wide.

Leipzig, at Fair time, was an exciting city, and the youngsters from the Zillertal at times felt lost in the bright and curious crowd. But they did just what they did at home when their spirits needed lifting—they sang together. The song they sang most, because it was their favorite, was "Song from Heaven."

Karl Mauracher, far-famed Zillertal organ builder, had taught the children the song. Once he had been called to a neighborhood village to repair an organ, and when his work was done, he had asked the organist to try it out. The organist was Franz Gruber, and somehow he slipped into the Christmas melody he had composed for Father Mohr.

"I never heard that song before," the organ builder said with awe in his voice. "Would you mind if I took it with me? Folks back where I live would appreciate it." Gruber had offered to write it down, but Mauracher told him that he knew hundreds of songs, and one more would make no difference.

The song quickly became popular in his valley, and was called "Song from Heaven." The organ builder didn't realize that he had brought back a truly valuable gift from two composers unknown to the entire world.

The children found the song's charm worked in the busy city;

passersby stopped to listen and were enchanted by the beautiful, melodious tune. One day an elderly gentleman, who introduced himself as Mr. Pohlenz, Director General of Music in the kingdom of Saxony, gave them tickets to one of the concerts that he conducted regularly in the Gewandhaus, the ancient guild house of the drapers of Leipzig. The youngsters were delighted.

When they entered the brilliantly lighted auditorium filled with silk-hatted gentlemen and ladies in rustling gowns, they felt timid and were glad to be led to inconspicuous seats beneath the platform. They were still rapt and glowing at the concert's end, when the shock came. For Mr. Pohlenz rose to announce that there were four children present with the finest voices he had heard in years. They might be persuaded to treat Their Royal Majesties, the King and Queen of Saxony, who were present, and the audience to some of their lovely Tyrolean airs.

The announcement took the youngsters' breath away, and their faces flamed as people began to applaud. "Let's just shut our eyes and pretend we're singing at home," Maly whispered to the others.

Their first song was "Song from Heaven," and when they had finished it, there was a moment of almost reverent quiet before applause broke loose. They sang all the songs they knew, and when they knew no more, they sang "Song from Heaven" again.

The audience was still shouting for more when a gentleman in uniform came up on the platform and said that Their Majesties desired to receive the singers.

"That was very pretty indeed," the King said after the children had been introduced. "We've never heard that Christmas song before. What is it?"

"It is a Tyrolean folk song, Your Highness," said Joseph.

"Won't you come to the castle and sing it on Christmas?" the Queen asked. "Our children will love it."

So it happened that on Holy Eve of the year 1832, in the Royal Saxon Court Chapel in Pleissenburg Castle, the Strasser children sang at the end of the Christmas services:

" 'Silent night! holy night!
All is calm, all is bright,

Round yon Virgin Mother and Child!
Holy Infant, so tender and mild,
Sleep in heavenly peace,
Sleep in heavenly peace.' "

And on that Christmas Eve the song bade the children farewell, to spread quietly around the world.

For years, on each Holy Eve, "Silent Night" was sung in the village of Hallein, in the house where Gruber lived and died, by a choir accompanied by Gruber's grandson, who used his grandfather's original guitar in the accompaniment. Later this yearly performance was carried round the world by radio—until a day in 1938 when the land of Austria was wiped off the map, and the little song of peace became "undesirable."

But the great land of music from which it hails knows no frontiers. And the "Song from Heaven," like the Christmas message itself, still rings for all men of goodwill, and has since found its way again into the country where it was born.

CANADA

Christmas in a French-Canadian Home

MARGUERITE DE ANGELI

CHRISTMAS was coming! Christmas was coming! Soon! Suzanne could feel it in the air. She knew it by the whisperings, by the way Tante Eugénie quickly hid things when she came in from school; and every morning there were mysterious shavings on the floor in the kitchen. She could tell, too, by the carols that Sister Marie was teaching them. Thick snow was falling. It creaked under her shoes. The church bell, when it rang, sounded cold, just as it always sounds at Christmas. Most exciting of all, when she went to the post office there was a package addressed to "Suzanne Pouliot." It was from the United States. There was a sticker on it that said, DO NOT OPEN UNTIL CHRISTMAS! It was very exciting. Suzanne could hardly keep from peeking. It was the first package she had ever had from the United States.

Of course, Suzanne couldn't find anything in the mail-order book that she could buy for Tante Eugénie or Uncle Jacques. She had only the little money she had earned last summer when she and Thérèse, her friend, sold huckleberries to the tourists. It was the first money she had ever had to spend for Christmas. But one day when she had walked home with Thérèse, they talked about Christmas and named over all the things they wished for: dolls and doll furniture, skis, sleds, and showshoes. Then they whispered about the gifts they would like to give, and Suzanne told about the lovely pictures of bottles of perfume, and lace handkerchiefs for ladies, and beautiful, warm slippers for men that she had seen in the catalog. But when she had tried to find something she could buy, everything cost too much. It was very sad.

"I know," Thérèse said, "in my daddy's store there are some lovely things you could get for M'sieur and Madame Pouliot. I will stop with you while you ask her if you can come home with me, eh? You could stay all night."

"*Oui, oui*, that would be fun!" Suzanne danced along in the snow, sending a spray of the fine, dry crystals into the air.

When she thought about Christmas, about the scarf for André, about going with André to get the tree, and about the manger scene with the little Christ-child, she felt as if she could fly like the gulls overhead.

It was so cold that the girls ran as far as they could before they had to stop for breath. Their noses and their cheeks were red as apples, but warm, knitted caps covered their ears and kept them from freezing. Both girls wore knitted mittens, too, but Suzanne had lost one of her own mittens, so she had to wear an old one of Berthe's on one hand. It had a hole in it, so she had to keep the end tucked in.

As they opened the door, Tante Eugénie turned from the little closet under the stairs with a secret look on her face. She must have heard Rogue barking! Suzanne knew there was a surprise hidden there, but she wouldn't look for anything. Thérèse was first to speak.

"Madame Pouliot, could Suzanne come to my house to stay to sleep?"

Tante Eugénie looked surprised. "So? You 'av not a good bed at 'ome?"

Suzanne took hold of her arm and coaxed with her best smile. "Please, Tante Eugénie, please! I promise to be good."

"But de Madame Ryan, she is not min'?" said Tante Eugénie.

"Oh, no, she won't mind! She loves company. Please, Madame Pouliot!" Thérèse was hardly through asking before Suzanne was on her way upstairs to get her nightgown and the money she had tucked way back in the bureau drawer.

When she came down again, André had come in with his books. He said he had to go to the blacksmith's for Uncle

Jacques and would hitch Rogue to the long sled and take them to Thérèse's.

"So," said Tante Eugénie, "you mus' take dis ol' coat for sit on. Eet is get colder tonight. Suzanne, put dis odder jacket under de coat."

Then she wrapped an old striped scarf tight around Suzanne's throat and helped her tuck her coat sleeves into the wrists of the mittens. "Tch! Tch! Holes, holes, holes! W'y you not take care of de mittens, eh? If *le bon Dieu* ever send more, you be more careful, no?"

Suzanne said, "Oh, *oui, oui.*" She was afraid Tante Eugénie might change her mind and not let her go.

When they arrived at the store, Mr. Ryan was alone. "Well, well, little ladies, what can I do for you today?" He made believe they were really grown up.

"We'd like to do some Christmas shopping, please." Thérèse flounced her dress as if it were a long one, and played "lady." Suzanne didn't feel as much at home with Mr. Ryan as with Uncle Jacques, so she just giggled and let Thérèse do the talking. Mr. Ryan asked how much money the young ladies wanted to spend, and showed them handkerchiefs, aprons, calendars, little coin purses, and oh, lots of nice things. It was very hard to decide what Tante Eugénie would like best. Suzanne looked at measuring cups, at a muffin tin, and at cream pitchers.

Tante did need a cream pitcher, and these were very pretty, with roses painted on the sides. She almost bought one, and then she spied the very thing! It looked lovely, it would be useful, and besides, it smelled of perfume. Best of all, it didn't cost such a great deal, and she would have a little left over. She bought it. With what was left, she bought some tobacco for Uncle Jacques. Mr. Ryan told her he thought she was a very good shopper, and wrapped the packages neatly and tied them with red string to make them look like Christmas.

Thérèse and Suzanne went to the house, at the back, and found Mrs. Ryan taking the fresh bread out of the oven. She wiped her hands and greeted Suzanne with a smile.

After supper, the girls did their lessons. It was warm in the kitchen, and it made them so sleepy that when Thérèse's mamma told them it was time to go to bed they were glad to do so.

It was only a few days till Christmas, now, and the next day André said it was time to go to the woods for a tree.

The best place to get the Christmas tree was over in the woods across the cove. André had seen just the right one when he was gathering wood, that day he fell into the water. After school he and Suzanne took the sled to bring the tree home. The air was frosty and clear, and the sled ran smoothly over the snow with Rogue to pull it. He let out short, sharp barks of delight as he flew along with his tail waving.

Away they went, down the road, through the empty fish flakes, across the beach and the frozen cove. When they reached the woods, André seemed to know just where the tree stood, and soon found it. "Oh, *bon! Bon!*—good!" Suzanne clapped her hands. "It will reach to the ceiling!" André raised his hatchet and leaned over to cut away some of the lower branches, then sent out a long whistle. "Look!" he shouted. "*Regarde!* It is Pepere's ax! It is not at the bottom of the cove at all!" The ax was leaning against the tree with just the top of the handle showing. When André lifted it out of the snow, it was covered with rust, but André knew how to clean off rust. How glad he was to see that ax! He had worried about it all winter. But Pepere didn't seem to know that it had been lost because André had taken good care to keep the wood boxes filled, himself, so that Pepere wouldn't need his favorite ax.

André took off his coat and set about chopping down the tree. It was strong and sturdy, so it took some good, hard work to cut it, and by the time it fell with a resounding crash, he was breathing hard.

He and Suzanne dragged the tree to the edge of the wood where Rogue waited with the sled. André had brought an old piece of rope with which he tied the tree to the sled, and they started for home. Suzanne jumped onto the soft branches of the tree and rode on the sled; André ran beside Rogue, and so, back they went across the ice.

All the morning, on the day before Christmas, the house was filled with excitement and bustle. The kitchen was full of many good smells, for Tante Eugénie was baking all kinds of things.

For the past two weeks she had been baking cookies and cakes, and several crocks full stood on the shelf.

The rabbits were dressed and cleaned, ready for the *réveillon ragout*. The pea soup was bubbling on the back of the stove all ready for supper. The lovely tree stood in its corner of the parlor, with the angel at the top, and candles on the tips of the branches ready to be lighted. All the house was shining clean.

Suzanne, Tante Eugénie, and Berthe were dressed in their best, waiting for Uncle Jacques and André to be ready. Cippy and Paule were scrubbed and dressed, Cippy's hair in little damp curls and Paule's tied back with a ribbon. It seemed like Sunday, but of course it wasn't! It was almost Christmas Eve! Pretty soon, Uncle Jacques called in the door, and they all went to the church for confession before Midnight Mass.

When they came back, each one brought to Tante Eugénie his gifts for the tree from their hiding places. Such mystery! Such tiptoeing! Suzanne saw Uncle Jacques come out of the door to the parlor, and close it quickly behind him. She heard a rustle of paper and saw Tante Eugénie slip something behind her as she closed the door to the little cupboard under the stairs. André kept something under his coat until he got past the kitchen; then he gave it to Tante, who opened the door just a crack. They whispered for a moment; then the door was shut again. It was hard to keep Cippy and Paule from seeing. They were all eyes and ears, and so excited they couldn't keep still. Every time the parlor door opened they craned their necks to see.

"*Va t'en! Va t'en!*—Go away!" Tante Eugénie scolded. Then they would be good for a few minutes, and turn somersaults all over the kitchen. They nearly squashed Pouf, so he took refuge under the stove.

Suzanne brought downstairs the gifts she had, and whispered to Uncle Jacques to put them on the tree for her. She didn't want Tante Eugénie to even see the package that smelled like perfume. She had wrapped the scarf in a piece of red tissue that Mr. Ryan had given her, and had written a name carefully on each package. Pepere sat quietly by the stove smoking his pipe. He didn't seem very much excited, but he looked happy.

Tante Eugénie kept going back and forth, into the kitchen, up the stairs, into the little cupboard, even down to the cellar. What could be down there! Cippy and Paule got down on their hands and knees to look when the trap door was open but they couldn't see, and when Tante came up, she kept whatever it was under her apron.

It seemed to Suzanne that the time would never come for the tree and the *réveillon.* She got out her pencil and tablet, and began to draw a picture of the tree. She wished again she had some paints like the tourist lady had. The colors would be so lovely on her picture.

It was dark before Tante Eugénie and Uncle Jacques had everything ready. Since the day before Christmas is a fast day, there was only pea soup for supper. The little ones must say their prayers and go to bed to rest until time for the Midnight Mass. Suzanne thought she never could go to sleep, but she was soon deep in dreams.

She was wakened by Berthe, who took her hand and whispered so as not to wake Cippy and Paule. They were too small to go and Pepere was too old, so he stayed at home with them.

They must all wrap up well; it was cold. Suzanne wished she hadn't lost her mitten, but the old one of Berthe's was better than none, and she would walk beside Uncle Jacques and put her hand in his.

As they turned out of the lane, people were coming from farther down the road, crunching along in the snow, the frosty air making their voices sound close.

"*Joyeux Noël!* Merry Christmas!" they called as they passed. "*Noël, Noël!*" The church bells began to ring. Suzanne shivered with excitement and looked up at the stars that filled the sky. One star looked especially bright. It looked as if it stood right over the church, and Suzanne thought it might be the Star of Bethlehem!

"So," said Uncle Jacques, as he squeezed her hand, "it is Noël! You are 'appy, eh, Ti-Su?" He swept her along beside him, her feet scarcely touching the ground.

"Oh, *oui!*" Suzanne laughed back at him, and skipped as much as she could skip with the heavy boots on her feet.

All along the way to the church, dark figures joined them from each lane and gateway. From each one came the greeting, "*Joyeux Noël! Joyeux Noël!*"

The church looked beautiful. The pillars were wrapped with greens, there were branches of evergreen on the windowsills, and a tall pine tree stood at each side of the altar. Soft candlelight showed the gilt edge on the Virgin's blue robe, reflected in the gold altar service, lighted the figure of a saint, and made real the little carved figures of the crèche at the left of the altar. The shepherds were kneeling in real straw, the Ste. Vierge was sitting on a real little wooden bench, and the tiny Christ-child was lying in a real little manger made of wood. Suzanne could see it all very plainly from where she was sitting. Softly, the choir began to sing "*Adeste Fidelis.*" Then the altar boys, two by two, with lighted candles, came slowly down the aisle. The tiny ones first, Étienne and little Jean, then Paul and Leonard and the others, the older ones next, and then the big boys like André and Jules. They looked very solemn, and hardly like the same boys that played so roughly every day.

After the service, Tante Eugénie invited Ol' Batees' to come home with them to the *réveillon.* He was glad to come and said he would bring his fiddle.

Such laughing and talking! Such a shouting of "Happy Christmas!" Everyone was in a good humor; everyone seemed very happy.

It didn't take long for Tante Eugénie to get the supper on the table. Uncle Jacques got out the jug of homemade wine and Ol' Batees' got out his fiddle.

Suzanne and André and Berthe danced around the kitchen. "Ol' Batees', he dance too," he said, his thick boots clumping on the floor.

The fire in the stove was snapping and cracking, the teakettle was humming, the fiddle was singing under Ol' Batees' fingers, the children were laughing and dancing.

Then Tante Eugénie called them all to the table. All was quiet for a moment while they blessed themselves, then all broke into happy cries of "*Joyeux Noël!*" as they sat down to the feast.

Then came the time for the gifts. Suzanne's throat ached with excitement. Cippy and Paule were standing at the door of the parlor, waiting for Uncle Jacques to carry in the lamp and to light the candles on the tree. At last he threw open the door. There stood the beautiful tree with little packages tied all over it, and at the base! Oh, Suzanne just couldn't believe her eyes! She sat down on the floor with the other children, in front of Pepere and Tante Eugénie. Uncle Jacques was to hand out the gifts.

"Aha!" he said, "here is somet'ing for good little girls." To Cippy he gave a cradle and to Paule a small cart. There were warm socks for Uncle Jacques, for Pepere, and for André, that Tante Eugénie had knitted, a dress for Berthe that Tante Eugénie had made from one of her own. Then Uncle Jacques picked up and hid behind him what Suzanne had seen peeking out from under the tree. She saw Uncle Jacque's eyes twinkle as he looked at her.

"So," he said, "now de *peti'* Suzanne can go, *vite! vite!* over de snow." And he gave her the most beautiful pair of snowshoes she had ever seen. She was so happy she hugged them to her and didn't say a word, but put them down long enough to throw her arms around Uncle Jacques as far as they would go. Next, came a pair of skis for André. "So that is why there were always wood splinters on the floor in the mornings!" André was as delighted as Ti-Su.

Suzanne held her breath while André unwrapped the scarf. She wanted to see what Tante Eugénie would say, too, when she saw it.

"I made it all myself!" she said as André's eyes opened in surprise. "Tch! Tch!" said Tante, "you mak' de weave?" She held up the scarf and shook her head. "Eet is beautiful!"

Then Ol' Batees' said, " 'Ere ees somet'ing soft for de little Suzanne," and threw it into her lap. She undid the wrapping with fingers that trembled. Oh, that good Tante Eugénie! She had knitted a new pair of red mittens for Suzanne. That was what she had been hiding in the little cupboard under the stairs for such a long time.

Then Uncle Jacques reached up and took off the tree the little package Suzanne had bought for Tante Eugénie.

"Um-m," he said, "it smell good. Gif' for a lady!" And gave it to Tante Eugénie. Suzanne could hardly wait till she took off the red string and undid the paper. Maybe she wouldn't like it. But how could she help it? It was so sweet. Tante Eugénie took off the last scrap of paper, and what do you think it was? A little cupid made of soap! Tante Eugénie did like it, even if her eyes were filled with tears. Grown-ups don't usually get presents. Then Uncle Jacques handed to Suzanne the package from the United States. Everyone watched to see what was in that package! Suzanne opened it. A card dropped out: "For Ti-Su who would love to paint!" And there was a box of beautiful water-colors and brushes from the tourist lady!

The candles were burning low and all the gifts had been taken from the tree. It was almost morning, and Cippy was yawning. Paule was asleep against Berthe's shoulder, Pepere was nodding in his chair, and Tante Eugénie could hardly keep her eyes open.

Ol' Batees' said, "*Merci*, madame, for de good *réveillon*," and once again he said, "*Joyeux Noël!*" and left.

What a happy time it had been! André went up to the loft, and all the children went up the stairs to bed, with Berthe to help them. Suzanne didn't even notice the long shadows up the wall; she knew that the strange bundle on the chair was only Tante Eugénie's old dress, that the moaning sound she heard was only the wind in the sycamore tree.

She heard the sleepy murmuring of Cippy and Paule as they said their prayers for Berthe. She said her own and crept into bed. She sighed with happiness at the thought of the snowshoes and the mittens and the beautiful paints; of how André had loved the scarf she had made him; of how Tante Eugénie loved the sweet little soap baby; and of how Uncle Jacques would enjoy the tobacco. She opened her eyes once more, and there, shining in her window, was the bright star. It shone softly and seemed to say, "*Joyeux Noël, Joyeux Noël.*"

CHINA

God's Christmas Gift to Rare Coral

STELLA M. RUDY

THE NIGHT was cold and cheerless. The north wind blew the chilly rain through the cracks of the bamboo hut. Mrs. Chan hugged her fire basket and said, "It is truly seven coats cold tonight."

The children were asleep behind the dark-blue mosquito net in the bed across the room. Mrs. Chan was making shoes which she sold for a living. Rare Coral was helping her. The peanut-oil lamp burned dimly, and with each strong gust of wind it flickered and almost went out.

"The famine has been hard on everybody," sighed Mrs. Chan. "People are not even buying shoes. They need money for rice. I really don't know what we shall do."

"Isn't there anything more we can sell?" asked Rare Coral.

"Nothing but Lustrous Gem," said Mrs. Chan. "She would bring more money than Glory Flower, but how can we part with her?"

Mrs. Chan tried to stop the falling tears with the back of her hand. Then she pulled up a corner of her coat to wipe them. Since the dreadful war had come to China she had had a hard struggle to made ends meet. Mr. Chan and the eldest son had gone to the front many moons before, and nothing had been heard of them since. Then had come the famine, and rice soared to the most unheard-of prices. Poor people just could not afford to eat. Yet thus far, she had been able to give them a bowl of rice each day, with now and then a little vegetable, such as spinach, for flavor. Friends had saved scraps of cloth with which she made shoes. She had received good prices for shoes for a while, but after this dreadful war had come to China, shoes were not so important as food, and many went barefooted even during the cold winter days.

"What else can we do?" Mother Chan sighed as she glanced at the few scraps and one or two finished pairs of shoes that might be sold. "Oh, if this war were only over!"

Rare Coral's eyes filled with tears. She loved Lustrous Gem dearly. How could she give her up? Had she not led them all to love the true God? She thought of how her little face had brightened as she came home from the kindergarten each day when things were still peaceful in this faraway village, and told the wonderful stories of the foreigner's God. They did not know then that he was their God too.

Then she thought of the time when Lustrous Gem had been very ill, and had begged her to pray to the true God. Tears blinded her eyes so that she could scarcely push the needle through the heavy sole of the shoes she was making. Rare Coral had never prayed to the true God before. She only knew how to pray to lifeless gods. But her little sister had begged her to pray to the true God, and she was oh, *so* sick!

Rare Coral had fled to the corner of the room where the Goddess of Mercy, black with age, was staring down upon her from the idol shelf. She had knelt before the idol and prayed most earnestly. She had even bumped her head nine times on the mud floor before the idol.

Lustrous Gem could not see her sister, but she heard her pray. "Don't pray to the Goddess of Mercy," she had cried. "That is only a piece of china, such as our rice bowls are made of. Pray to the *true* God. I'm oh, so very sick—so very sick!" The last words had been very faint and Lustrous Gem had closed her eyes wearily. Then had come a little fainter plea, "Pray to the true God."

"I don't know how to pray to the foreigner's God," Rare Coral had sobbed in distress. Then she thought of the prayer she had heard Lustrous Gem pray:

"Jesus, tender Shepherd, hear me;
Bless thy little lamb tonight.

Through the darkness be thou near me,
Keep me safe till morning light."

She had knelt down beside the bed as she had seen Lustrous Gem do, and had repeated the prayer with her eyes closed. When she had finished praying, Lustrous Gem opened her eyes and smiled up into her face.

That night Rare Coral had repeated the verse over and over again. She never closed her eyes all night, but watched anxiously over the little one. In the morning Lustrous Gem had asked for rice gruel, and from that time on she had improved.

That was the beginning of Rare Coral's knowledge of the true God.

Later Mrs. Chan had begun to inquire into this new strange doctrine of another God and had soon lost faith in lifeless idols. She had still much to learn, and now that they were facing starvation, she saw no other plan than to sell Lustrous Gem.

"But how can we part with her?" sobbed Rare Coral quietly. "Did she not lead us to the kind, tender Shepherd? Surely he will help us now!"

But in spite of everything Lustrous Gem was sold. She was taken across the river to live with strangers. Her little heart was nearly broken.

The hut seemed dreadfully quiet after she left. Mrs. Chan was very sad, but she had lived in the country of China all her life and this was not unusual. Children were sold in order that the rest of the family might live. Rare Coral wept day and night.

Christmas was drawing near, but there would be no Christmas joy without Lustrous Gem to brighten the day with her merry little voice in song and laughter. The hut had never seemed so dreary. It was dark and gray and cheerless. All the joy had gone out of Rare Coral's life. It was only when she prayed to the tender Shepherd that she found peace in the "middle of her heart."

The day before Christmas, Rare Coral went slowly to the chapel. Her heart was heavier than it had ever been. She tried to smile as she entered, but seeing the bright faces of the other children made her long more than ever for her little sister. Tears filled her eyes in spite of her efforts to hide them. She quickly wiped them away, for she did not want anyone to see her cry.

"I have good news for you, Rare Coral," said the missionary, smiling. Her face was radiant as she held out a letter and check. "Someone away over in America sent this money and said that it was to be used for someone in great need. With it we can redeem Lustrous Gem!"

Rare Coral was quite overcome by the news, and burst into tears—tears of joy. Could it be possible that her dear little sister would spend Christmas Day with them? Her joy was too great for any expression in words. All she could say was, "Thank the heavenly Father!"

Never was there a happier celebration of the glad Christmas Day than there was in the old, gray, dark, bamboo hut, brightened now by the cheer of Lustrous Gem. Their bowl of rice needed no extra vegetable for flavor now as they sat with bowed heads to thank the true God for the scanty meal before them. To them it was better than the most savory feast.

"You are God's Christmas gift to us," whispered Rare Coral as she clasped her little sister once more in her arms.

CZECHOSLOVAKIA

Maminka's Children's Christmas Dream and Joys

ELIZABETH ORTON JONES

"MAMINKA!" shouted Nanka, running down the stairs to the kitchen. "Four more days till Christmas!"

"Yes, my little mouse, I know," said Maminka. "*Na*, run along!"

"Aunt Pantsy!" shouted Nanka, running up the stairs again. "Four more days till—"

"Christmas!" said Aunt Pantsy, giving Nanka a hug. "Run along, my good girl!"

"Old Grampa!" shouted Nanka, running down the stairs again. She opened the door to his room. "Four more days—Yi! Is that your secret, Old Grampa?"

Old Grampa motioned her to come in, and to shut the door behind her. Nanka tiptoed round Old Grampa's bed to where he sat by the window, whittling with his sharp knife.

Whittle-whittle-whittle! went Old Grampa's sharp knife.

On Old Grampa's table stood a tiny stable, with a roof of straw.

"What is here?" asked Nanka.

And Old Grampa answered, "Betlem." Then he held out two tiny persons for her to see.

She took one in each hand, very carefully.

One was a man with a bald head and a beard. He had a long robe on. He was bending over.

"What's his name?" asked Nanka.

"Josef," answered Old Grampa.

The other tiny person was a woman, with a halo on her head. She was kneeling and reaching out her hands.

"What's her name?" asked Nanka.

"Maria," answered Old Grampa.

Nanka put Josef and Maria, very carefully, inside the stable. Then she rested her chin on the edge of the table, and looked and looked and looked, because she loved the tiny Josef and the Maria that Old Grampa had made out of wood.

Next morning there were only three more days till Christmas.

"Old Grampa!" shouted Nanka, knocking at his door. "Three more days!" Then she opened the door and slipped inside.

There was no sound in Old Grampa's room but the whittle-whittle-whittle! of his sharp knife. He sat by the window, making three more tiny persons out of wood. When they were finished, he held them out for Nanka to see.

They were kings, with fancy crowns on and with long robes and cloaks. Two had long beards, and one held a little round box. The long-bearded two were bending over, like Josef. The one with the box was kneeling, like Maria.

"Who are these?" asked Nanka.

"*Kraly*," answered Old Grampa.

Nanka put the Kraly, very carefully, beside the stable, where Josef and Maria were. Then she rested her chin on the edge of the table, and looked and looked and looked, because she loved the tiny Kraly that Old Grampa had made out of wood.

Next morning there were only two more days till Christmas.

"Old Grampa!" shouted Nanka, knocking at his door. "Two more days!" And she opened the door and slipped inside.

Old Grampa had already finished two more tiny persons, and he was whittling a third with his sharp knife.

The two were angels with wings on. One of them, the smaller, was carrying flowers. The other was carrying fruit.

"What's her name?" asked Nanka, touching, very carefully, the wings of the one who was carrying fruit.

"Marianka," answered Old Grampa.

"What's her name?" asked Nanka, quickly pointing to the tinier wings of the one who was carrying flowers.

"Nanka," said Old Grampa quietly.

"Yi!" said Nanka not so quietly.

Then Old Grampa finished the other tiny person. It was a little boy, with a big hat on. He was kneeling, like Maria, and carrying fruit, like Marianka.

"Honzichek!" guessed Nanka right away.

And Old Grampa nodded his head.

Nanka put the three, very carefully, beside the stable, where Josef and Maria and the Kraly were. Then she rested her chin on the edge of the table, and looked and looked and looked, because she loved the tiny Nanka, the Marianka, and the Honzichek that Old Grampa had made out of wood.

Next morning was the morning of Christmas Eve.

"Old Grampa!" shouted Nanka, opening his door. "Christmas Eve!" She ran to the table where the stable stood.

And there, at last, by Maria, lay the tiniest baby that Nanka had ever seen, on some hay, with a tiny, wooden feather bed to cover Him.

"*Jezishek*," Old Grampa explained.

Maria was reaching out her hands to the tiny Jezishek. Josef was bending over him. The Kraly were bowing and kneeling. And Nanka, Marianka, and Honzichek were bringing flowers and fruit to him.

"You beautiful little Jezishek!" whispered Nanka.

Then she rested her chin on the edge of the table, and smiled and smiled and smiled. She loved the little Jezishek best of all.

Old Grampa nodded his head and wrinkled up his face as he put his sharp knife away. He loved the little Jezishek too!

It was going to be a very jolly party, with music and Christmas bread, and a good time for all.

"Maminka," said Honzichek, "do you think Mr. Kuna really will come?"

"I certainly hope so," said Maminka.

Honzichek ran to the window to see if he could see Mr. Kuna's express wagon coming down the road. But he could not see it—yet.

When the Christmas bread was all laid out, warm and brown and beautiful, on the kitchen table, and the good coffee was bubbling on the stove, Maminka said, "*Na*, my little mouse, my sweet raisin, and my rather small beetle, if you will call Old Grampa and Aunt Pantsy, Uncle Edy and Aunt Matylda, I'll go out and see if the other guests are ready to come to our party!" She reached for her shawl, threw it over her head, and went out into the snow.

Marianka began to call: "Old Gram-pa! Aunt Pant-sy!"

Nanka called: "Uncle Edy! Bring your zither!"

Honzichek ran to get his huge old accordion. Wawk! Wawk! SQUAWK! it went, as Honzichek made it go out and in. Oh, he was going to play today, for Maminka, for Mr. Kuna—for everybody to dance!

"Aunt Ma-tyl-dy!" called Honzichek in a loud voice.

Down the stairs came Uncle Edy, with his zither. Down came Aunt Pantsy. Old Grampa shuffled out of his room. Out of Nanka's room came Aunt Matylda, stepping high, in her embroidered stockings. They were all very much excited to be coming to a party.

The kitchen door opened, and in came Maminka, her shawl covered with snowflakes and her cheeks red as roses from the cold. In came the other guests with her.

Honzichek's Katcha waddled into the kitchen, in her beautiful red-knitted jacket, followed by Marianka's big, speckled Bidushka. The red hen and the white hen came next. And, last of all, in strutted the great green rooster.

"Where is Old Horse?" asked Nanka. "And Old Cow?"

"Well," explained Maminka, "they were afraid that they wouldn't be able to get through the door, because of being so big. They were sorry! They wanted to come very much!"

"Poor Old Horse! And poor Old Cow!" said Nanka. "Too big to come to our party!"

"Don't worry," said Maminka, "we'll take them some Christmas bread afterward, and sprinkle it over with oats and hay. That will make them very happy, I'm sure," said Maminka. "But where is Mr. Kuna? And where is our very smallest guest?"

"Smallest guest?" wondered Nanka.

"Where is Aunt Matylda's little mouse?" said Maminka.

"Ho-o!" giggled Nanka. "I guess it's in the little house! Is that where it is, Aunt Matylda?"

Aunt Matylda winked and nodded. Her tiny gold earrings nodded with her.

So Nanka went hippity-hop to get it. "Here comes the smallest guest!" she shouted, as she came back carrying, very carefully, the little wooden house.

Everybody gathered round, to see. Everybody but Uncle Edy. He sat down on a kitchen chair and began to play the tiniest, tinkliest tune in the world, on the high-up strings of his zither.

Nanka set the little house on the floor, and opened its door. First the little mouse looked through the door. Then it came out onto the floor. It tipped its little head and wiggled one ear. It heard the tune that Uncle Edy was playing! It tipped its head the other way, and wiggled its other ear. Then all of a sudden it began to do some little fancy mouse steps in a circle, round and round.

"*Pa-pri-ka-a!*" chuckled Honzichek. "It's dancing!"

But just at that moment Uncle Edy stopped playing, for he heard footsteps outside. Wide open flew the kitchen door, and there stood Mr. Kuna.

"Mr. Kuna! There you are!" shouted Nanka, Marianka, and Honzichek.

"Cluckety-awk! Cluck! Cluck!" said Bidushka.

"Woodle! Wack!" sang Katcha.

The great green rooster flew up to the back of the stove and crowed, "Rooka-roodle-oodle-oo!"

And the little mouse quickly climbed back into its house and sat down, as if to say—in Bohemian, of course—"Well, Mr. Kuna, now the party can begin!"

"Ho!" laughed Mr. Kuna as he took off his coat. "Ho!" he laughed as he looked round at everybody. He looked at all the chickens, the big goose wearing a jacket, and the little mouse in its house. He looked at Uncle Edy's zither, and at Honzichek's huge old accordion, and at Maminka's beautiful Christmas bread laid out on the kitchen table. He smelled the good coffee, bubbling on the stove. "Ho! Ho! Ho! Ho!" laughed jolly Mr. Kuna, rubbing his hands together.

He had never been invited to a party like this in all his life before!

When the party was over, Katcha and the chickens went out to the barn again and to the chicken house. And Maminka took some Christmas bread to Old Horse and Old Cow, just as she said she would do.

But everybody wanted Mr. Kuna to stay for a quiet little supper round the kitchen table. Maminka made *brambory* soup for supper—good *brambory* soup, with noodles and mushrooms. And she filled cup after cup full of Old Cow's sweet milk.

Maminka set the kitchen table in a lovely way. In the middle stood a little tree, with long red apple peelings looped over its branches and a candle on the top of it. The candle was lighted!

Under the tree were the Maria and Josef, the Kraly, the angels, the little boy, and the tiny Jezishek—all the beautiful things that Old Grampa had made out of wood. But now they were more beautiful than ever, for Uncle Edy had painted them in red and blue and brown and gold. And the light from the lighted candle shone down through the branches of the little tree, making those colors bright.

After supper there were apples to eat. Mr. Kuna chose a big red shiny one.

"There must be a perfect star inside this apple," he said.

"A star, Mr. Kuna?" asked Nanka, Marianka, and Honzichek, very much surprised. "A star in an apple?"

"Why, bless you!" said Mr. Kuna. "Didn't you know that? There's a star in every apple!"

"When I was a little girl in the old country," said Maminka, "we used to cut an apple open every Christmas Eve. We always hoped that we would find a perfect star, for that meant health and happiness during all the coming year."

"Yes," said Mr. Kuna, "when I was a little boy in the old country, we used to do the same. Let's do it now! Let's cut this apple!" And he handed the big shiny apple to Old Grampa.

Everyone leaned close while Old Grampa took out his sharp knife. They all held their breath while he cut the apple quickly, crossways through the core, then opened it very, very slowly.

There it was! A perfect star!

"Oh! Oh!" said Marianka.

And everyone looked very happy.

"Our star!" said Maminka, smiling. "Our Christmas star! Every one of us will be healthy and happy. Every single one!"

Marianka looked at the Christmas star. She looked at her mother and her grandfather, at her brother and her little sister, and at the others, gathered so close together. She looked at the tiny Jezishek, under the tree, and at all the beautiful things round him. And then Marianka whispered: "Maminka—you know what? I feel like saying my prayers, right here by the kitchen table!"

"I think we all feel that way, my sweet raisin," said Maminka, bowing her head. Nanka, Marianka, and Honzichek bowed their heads too. And Mr. Kuna bowed his. And Old Grampa, Aunt Pantsy, Uncle Edy, and Aunt Matylda all bowed their heads while Maminka said a little prayer.

"Our Father," said Maminka, "we pray that the Jezishek may be born in our hearts tonight, as he was born in Betlem long ago."

For a few minutes everyone was very still. Then they were all smiling and talking again.

Mr. Kuna put on his coat, thanked them for a lovely time, and went out into the snow, to drive home in his express wagon.

Nanka, Marianka, and Honzichek got undressed.

Aunt Pantsy folded the feather bed over them.

Maminka blew out the candle at the top of the little tree and said good night.

And soon they were sound asleep.

While Marianka was asleep in the big, soft feather bed, she dreamed a dream.

The little star which they had found in the apple grew, in Marianka's dream, to a great star. It was a great, perfect star. And it was shining on the roof of the barn. Up where the little weather vane usually stood, it was shining. It made the night as bright as morning.

Marianka dreamed that she woke up and saw it. She dreamed that she woke Nanka up too, and Honzichek.

"Wake up, Nanka! Honzichek!" said Marianka, in her dream. "The Christmas star is shining! It's shining on our barn!"

Nanka and Honzichek woke up—but only in Marianka's dream. And, all together, they got up and tiptoed across the kitchen. Out into the snow they tiptoed, in their bare feet. But the snow didn't feel cold at all. It felt only soft, like feathers. They ran across the soft snow to the barn. And Honzichek pulled at the high old door. It creaked on its hinges, as usual.

Then they heard a little cry inside. It was a sweet little cry. It sounded like a baby, waking.

And somebody whispered, "Who is there?"

Honzichek pulled the door open, and they all peeked in. Marianka dreamed that they saw Old Horse and Old Cow standing together. Old Horse was breathing big sweet breaths. And Old Cow was mooing, quite softly. Katcha was sitting down in the hay. The red hen and Bidushka, the white hen and the great green rooster, were sitting in a row, on a board. And a little sparrow was perched on the edge of Old Cow's manger.

In the hay, by the manger, a woman was kneeling. She looked like Maminka. But her name was Maria.

A man was bending over Maria—he looked like Old Grampa. But his name was Josef. And there, in Old Cow's manger, the dear baby Jezishek lay!

"May we come in?" asked the children, in Marianka's dream.

And, in her dream, the mother Maria nodded. Of course they could come!

So they tiptoed through the hay and knelt down beside the manger.

And, just before the end of Marianka's dream, the dear baby Jezishek looked up at them—and smiled!

On Christmas Day in the morning the great green rooster crowed, "Rooka-roodle-oodle-oodle-oodle-oo!"

A little sparrow cheeped. Old Horse stamped his foot in the barn. Old Cow swished some hay.

And Nanka, Marianka, and Honzichek jumped out of Aunt Matylda's feather bed.

They tiptoed to Old Grampa's door and softly opened it. They tiptoed across Old Grampa's room and slowly and carefully, so as not to waken him, pulled something out from its safe hiding place underneath Old Grampa's bed.

It was the big goose-feather pillow which they had made for Maminka. It was covered with three kinds of cloth, red, and blue, and brown, sewn together, crisscross, with white thread. At each of the pillow's three corners was a little red button, and out of each red button hung a blue tassel. There were long brown fringes round the edges of the pillow. And right on top a big red heart was embroidered. In the middle of the red heart were three embroidered letters—an *N*, an *M*, and an *H*.

Marianka and Honzichek carried the pillow out of Old Grampa's room, while Nanka quietly shut his door. Then, with the pillow, they all scrambled up the stairs to Maminka's room.

"My little mouse, my swe-e-e-et raisin, my rather small beetle!" yawned Maminka, waking up. "Merry Christmas!"

"Merry Christmas, Maminka!" they said, holding the big pillow out to her.

"*Na!*" said Maminka, opening her eyes wide. "What is that?"

"A pillow, Maminka," explained Honzichek.

He nudged Marianka, Marianka nudged Nanka, and all together they pushed the pillow into Maminka's bed—until her head was resting on the big embroidered heart.

"Ah!" said Maminka. "It's very soft! Thank you, my little mouse, my swe-e-e-et raisin," she yawned, "my rather small beetle!" She closed her eyes. "You know," she whispered, with her eyes closed, "when I was a little girl in the old country, I used to pretend that I had three children—"

"Go to sleep again!" said Marianka, giving Maminka a kiss.

"—they helped me, and looked after me, and tucked me into bed—" whispered Maminka.

"Sleep and dream!" said Honzichek, smoothing her hair.

"—that's the kind of children they were—" whispered Maminka.

"Sleep and dream on your pillow!" said Nanka, tucking Maminka in. "We made it for you!"

"Hsh!" they said to one another.

Then they went softly tiptoeing down the stairs.

Marushka's Christmas Joys

LIBUSHKA BARTUSEK

I AM A GOOD BOY
I AM A GOOD BOY
I AM A GOOD BOY

"What is that you are writing, Yurka? May I see?" Yurka screwed up his tiny nose, which as yet had acquired no definite shape, and studied the large sheet of white paper.

"I am writing to Saint Nicholas, to let him know how I've behaved, and when he comes tomorrow night, I shall hand it to him. Is it written well?"

Marushka, who was already in her second year at school and therefore felt very wise, eyed the printed words critically. She was proud that Yurka had learned so much in such a short while in school and did not hesitate to tell him so. "However," she added, "I think I should not write that sentence any more. The good saint may suspect that you are trying to hide something from him, with so much writing. Just sign your name."

"And you might sign mine, too, because I'll not have time to write him a report this year," suggested Tomash, who was at the other end of the table, drawing colorful designs on a small wooden chest.

"For shame, Tomash!" cried Marushka. "Too lazy to write for yourself. I hope Saint Nicholas did not hear you!" and she pricked her finger with the embroidery needle. "That's what I get," she said to herself, "for scolding my own brother!"

Yurka signed his name. The letters of his name were twice as large as those in the sentences, although he had not meant them to be.

"Shall I put an ornament in the corner?" he asked.

"It would be very nice," answered Marushka.

"What shall it be?"

The question interested even Tomash, and all three thought for a long while. Suddenly the older brother spoke up. "As long as Saint Nicholas brings us fruit and nuts, why not make The Little Apple design?"

That was an excellent idea, the other two children agreed, and Yurka started immediately to make the first design a Moravian child learns to draw, The Little Apple. When he had finished, it looked very fine indeed, just like a real apple cut in half. One could see the core, the seed vessels and seeds, the stem at the bottom, and the bit of flower at the top. The colors Yurka used were not exactly natural, for it was painted in blue and yellow as well as red, green, and black. But no one would have any trouble at all recognizing The Little Apple.

The letter and drawing completed, Yurka folded it neatly and sighed. He had performed a delicate task with great dignity and he was satisfied that it was well done. Marushka and Tomash were too busy to pay much heed to what he was doing. Marushka was engrossed with the last row of cross-stitching on the linen square that she was making for Mamichka for Christmas, while Tomash was putting tiny black dots in the center of an ornament that he had made, and black dots needed one's undivided attention.

Yurka studied the room carefully. Where would the letter find the safest resting place until Saint Nicholas came? He considered the wardrobe. No, they had too many clothes hung in it, and the letter would be too easily swept out. The cupboard? His almost tragic experience with the powder in the cupboard made him suspicious of that hiding place.

Ah! At last he had it! The stove, the baking oven of the stove. It opened into the hallway, and no one would see him put it there, providing he made no noise. Today was Thursday. There would be no baking until Saturday, and tomorrow, just before Saint Nicholas would come, Yurka could get his precious letter. Yurka tiptoed out into the hallway to the oven door, quietly opened it, and slipped the beautiful paper into the opening.

Early the next morning Yurka was awakened by a most pleasant smell, the smell of baking bread. Anichka had been up and about for hours, and since there was so much to do before Sunday, she decided to do her baking today. Today! Why, today was Saint Nicholas' Eve! Saint Nicholas' Eve! Anichka baking in the baking oven, where he had put his beautiful letter that was to say so much for him!

"Anichka! Anichka! You've burned it! He won't see it! He won't see it!" Poor little Yurka was beside himself!

Kind Anichka tried hard to rescue the treasured letter, as soon as she was able to understand Yurka's frantic cries, but it was too late. The large sheet of white paper had turned the golden brown of a well-baked loaf of bread!

"Don't cry, Yurka! I'm very sorry. But I wouldn't worry too much, if I were you. After all, Saint Nicholas and his Angel may have been here during the night to see whether the chimney was clean enough for them to come through. Perhaps they had already read your letter!"

Yurka blinked away his tears. Perhaps this was true. Mamichka had told him that Saint Nicholas comes through the chimney, though she had never actually seen him do so. Besides, to be cross on the very day he was expected might bring a black mark against Yurka's name on the record. So he decided not to cry.

It seemed the day would never turn into dark night, but at last supper was over and the children sat down at the table, each one trying hard to do his work. Marushka had put away her finished linen square, but she was busily knitting a stocking. Mamichka was teaching her how to turn the heel, but Marushka was paying more attention to the door than to her mother. Yurka was trying to carve a funny wooden doll for Vavrova's baby, and Tomash was busy reading a storybook.

Knock! Knock! Yurka's heart skipped a beat. So did Marushka's. Tomash could not quite make up his mind whether to be excited or not. Tap, tap, tap. That was Saint Nicholas' staff. Rattle, rattle, rattle. That was the Devil's chain, and in walked the three—Saint Nicholas, tall and splendid-looking in his bishop's robe and mitre and flowing white beard; the Angel, in white draperies that were studded with stars; and finally the Devil himself, in a black suit that made him look like a chimney sweep. The Devil's face was as red and ugly as the Angel's was white and beautiful.

Saint Nicholas wasted no time. "I have many other places to go tonight," he explained. Although the children had been told to say their prayers as soon as the saint appeared, and prayers were to be said with downcast eyes, Tomash could not help stealing a glance at the Good One. . . . His voice sounded so much like the voice of Yanko the blacksmith, even though the sound was muffled by the long beard.

"Have you been good, Tomash?" Tomash was so startled out of his doubts by the thunderous question, he began to stutter, "I—I—I have tried."

"Indeed he has tried," and Mamichka's voice spoke reassuringly. Tomash was grateful to her.

"Put it in the book. And what would you like for Christmas?" asked Saint Nicholas.

"I should like a violin, if that's not asking too much."

"We shall see, we shall see. Put it in the book." And the Angel took great pains to write down everything carefully.

"And you, Marushka? What would you like?"

Marushka turned quite red and for all the promises she had made to herself that this year she would look Saint Nicholas in the eye, she found that her lids were too heavy to raise.

"Speak up, Marushka," urged her mother. "Saint Nicholas must be on his way. What would you like most of all?"

"I'd like—most of all—I'd like a baby sister!"

"Put it down, put it down." And the Angel wrote very quickly. "And if there are no baby sisters this year, there may be a doll that will look just like one."

Yurka was very hot one moment, and very cold the next. The Devil had a terrible way of rattling the chain and looking right at him. Yurka's tongue just simply stuck to the roof of his mouth!

"Well, well, this is the good boy, Yurka. This is the good boy who wrote me the long letter. You have his name, do you not, my good Angel?" And Saint Nicholas looked at the record book, "to make certain that the name was spelled correctly," he explained. Then he added: "What is it you want? Is it a horse?—a black horse like Yanko's?"

"That would be too big for Yurka," explained Mamichka. "Perhaps a smaller one, a black rocking horse would be better, good Saint," and Yurka nodded his approval.

"And now that you have been such well-behaved children, you may have these apples and nuts from our bag. Put them on the table, Devil! The Angel will carry his book up to heaven to the Christ-child, and there the Child will read the records. Then, on Christmas Eve, he will come to you and bring his gifts to you in memory of the gifts that were brought to him long, long ago." And before anyone could move, Saint Nicholas was gone, gone for another year.

It was so strange to be walking across the white snow, so very late at night, thought Marushka. An atmosphere of mystery and deep reverence seemed blended in the air. It was Christmas Eve, and everything was very, very still, everything except the crunch of the crisp snow beneath the feet of those on their way to church.

What a day it had been! A day full of happenings! For the first time in his life, Yurka was able to fast until suppertime!

"You shall see the Golden Pig," Mamichka had promised, "if you can manage not to eat a bite of anything until supper!"

Much to everyone's surprise, Yurka did hold out, and so he saw the Golden Pig race across the sitting room, just as he sat drawing in his book. Tomash was the only one of the three Horak children who had grown wise to the fact that Anichka flashed a mirror on the wall to make the Pig, but he was kind enough not to spoil the fun of the others by saying anything about it.

The other events of the day danced across Marushka's mind—sitting down to a delicious supper of mushroom soup, fish, and black gravy with prunes, dumplings; and last, but most important, cooked farina flavored with honey, butter, and ginger. Marushka remembered that this last food was exactly what the shepherds brought the little Christ-child as he lay in the manger. Then, scraps of the food and wafers were carried out to the animals in the stable. After that, the family gathered around a Christmas tree. It was gaily decorated with candies, fruits, and tiny candles. Here the gifts were distributed. A violin for Tomash, the rocking horse for Yurka, and the doll for Marushka were all there. And Marushka recalled that Mamichka and the rest of the grown-ups were so grateful for their gifts.

"Weren't the wireworkers kind to come to our door to sing tonight?" said Marushka, breaking the silence.

"To be sure, they were," Mamichka agreed. She knew why the little boys from Slovakia came to the Horak door each year, singing carols as they carried the little wood carvings of the Nativity. Tatichek never turned them away. A good meal and the night's lodging was their reward each Christmas Eve.

Marushka was in deep thought again. It was queer! Anichka had grown so red when, after everyone had thrown one boot each over his head, Anichka's boot pointed out, and Mamichka had laughingly said that surely Anichka would be the first to leave home. Tatichek had added, "Perhaps to get married!" Marushka hoped Anichka would not get married too soon! Suddenly, in the midst of the fun, had come the trumpet call, announcing High Midnight Mass, and now, here they were, trudging through the deep snow on their way to church.

"Oh, Anichka, you won't get married right away, will you?" whispered Marushka as they neared the church.

"Hush, child!" admonished Anichka. "We mustn't speak of those things now. This is the Child's night and we must think of nothing but him."

They were inside the church now, and soon the choir was singing. Tomash's voice could be heard above all the others in the choir as they sang the beautiful old Czech carols. The old organ, which was ordinarily very wheezy, took on a new and heavenly quality as it blended with the orchestra of village musicians.

Just before the close of Mass, fourteen shepherds from six different villages walked down the center aisle, carrying lighted candles. They were dressed in their simple shepherd cloaks, but they moved with great dignity as they neared the altar. Down the side aisles they went to the door of the church, where they each took a long, thin shepherd's horn, and moving up the center aisle again, stood, each at his station. All at once, as though they had rehearsed for weeks, they raised the horns to their lips and blew a long blast that could be heard for kilometers around.

"Where are they going now?" whispered Yurka as the shepherds filed out of the church.

"Home," replied Tatichek.

"But one of them is Uncle Skopek's man. Will he go home too?"

"Of course he will," was Tatichek's answer.

"Isn't it far to walk?" queried Yurka anxiously.

"The shepherds walked much farther than that to see the Babe and kneel at his feet."

By this time the Horak family had reached the door of the church. "See," said Tatichek, "each shepherd has a lantern and is on his way home."

Marushka watched the lights of the shepherds, until they looked like tiny Saint John flies, twinkling in the distance. Then she looked up into the sky, and seeing one star that shone brighter than the rest in the darkness above, murmured gently to herself, "Do you suppose that could be the same star that led the shepherds before?"

FINLAND

The Christmas Angel

MARGARET W. EGGLESTON

THE MOTHERS of the Settlement Mothers' Club were sitting about the open fire in the clubroom, enjoying a lighted tree and the stories that the Story Lady of the Settlement had been telling them. She had told "Babouska" for the Russian mothers; "Little Gretchen and the Wooden Shoe" for the German mothers; and "Piccola" for the Italian group. As she finished the last one, a voice in the rear of the room said: "Won't you please tell the story of the Christmas Angel? I am Finnish, and I love that story which the mothers of my country tell to their children."

The Story Lady suggested several stories of Christmas angels, none of which was the one to which the stranger had referred.

"Why not tell it yourself?" asked the Story Lady. "I don't think I know the one you like. Perhaps it will be such a good one that we shall all tell it at the bedtime hour tonight." The Finnish mother hesitated at first, but at last she told this story:

In the land of Finland, across the sea, the mothers do not tell of Santa. They tell of a beautiful Christmas Angel who goes from house to house on Christmas Eve, looking through the windows at the Christmas trees and presents. Sometimes she smiles; sometimes she shakes her head sadly. If the gifts on the trees have been prepared with love in the heart, no matter how small in size or cost the gifts may be, the fairy waves her wand over them, and then they are sure to bring happiness to the one to whom they go. If a gift is given only in return for one received, the Christmas Angel turns aside in sorrow and the gift will bring no real pleasure, no matter how much it may have cost. The Finnish children believe in the Christmas Angel, and they try to give with love.

Once upon a time, long and long ago, there lived in Finland a widow with her six children. Her husband had been killed by the falling of a tree, so they were very poor. The owner of the forest in that town had given the widow permission to gather what wood she needed, and also to put some into small bundles which the children could take about in a cart and sell. So the widow had moved into a tiny house at the very edge of the forest, and the wood that they sold bought their food and clothing.

Their little home had only two rooms: one downstairs and one, called a loft, above. A ladder went from the room below to the one above. At night a trapdoor was shut down when the widow and her children went to bed in the loft, lest some child should fall through the hole in the floor and be hurt.

As the first Christmas drew near after the father had died, the widow and the children all wondered how they could buy gifts for their tree, for they had no extra money. They talked it over and decided that each child should have only one present; then each would have to make or buy only one thing. The children could knit, and their mother had wool that had been made from their own sheep. This helped, for all needed mittens and scarves and caps.

As they went back and forth to work, they watched for a tree that would look well in their small room, and on the day before Christmas the whole family went to get the one chosen. Gregory cut it down; Alexander tied it on the sled; the smaller children tugged and pulled as they drew it home; and all helped to set it up. It was so high that there was hardly room at the top for the picture of the Christmas Angel, which always topped the Christmas trees in that part of Finland.

The children had no red or blue or silver balls, such as American children have for their Christmas trees, but they had big red apples from their own apple tree; strings of red berries that they had gathered on the hills; and red peppers grown in their tiny garden. They had several picture cards that they liked, so the tree was soon trimmed and ready.

As it grew dark, Alexander lighted a fire in the old fireplace, and it made the room look very beautiful to the children. They danced about the tree and sang a merry song; they brought the six packages containing their gifts and put them under the tree, and then they climbed the ladder to sleep on piles of straw in the loft. After the children had gone, their mother brought out six little packages of candy that she had made. She hung them on the tree, wiping her eyes on her blue gingham apron as she remembered what happy Christmas seasons they had always had together. Soon she too had climbed the ladder, closing the trapdoor behind her.

The children were still talking about their beautiful tree, of the good smells, and of the visit of the Christmas Angel. When the mother was once in bed, all were still, for all knew how tired she was after a long day in the woods.

Now, another mother and her children lived in that loft where the children were sleeping. It wasn't a mother cat and her kittens; nor a mother mouse and her babies; nor a mother dog and her puppies. You would never guess, so you will have to be told that it was a mother spider and her babies. Neither family bothered the other, so they were good friends.

Of course the spider babies were all fast asleep before the children came to the loft, but the mother spider heard every word that the children had said. She was greatly puzzled. What a strange tree, to be covered with peppers, and apples, and berries, all at once! She must surely go down to see it before morning, for she had never seen such a tree.

When all was still in the loft, the mother spider went tippy-toe, tippy-toe, tippy-toe across the floor, so as not to wake the children's tired mother. She crept through a crack under the trapdoor, and started to run down the ladder. Suddenly the dark room below her was flooded with light. Before the tree stood a beautiful lady, dressed in dazzling white. She had a silver wand in her hand, and her face was covered with smiles as she touched one and another of the Christmas packages, saying: "Every one is given with love in the heart. Every one! What a beautiful tree it is!"

At first the mother spider was very much afraid of the bright stranger, so she crept back of the ladder, out of sight. Then she decided that anyone with such a kind face would be good to a little animal, so she ran quickly down the ladder, stood before the lady, and made a pretty curtsy.

"Are you the Christmas Angel that the children were talking about?" she asked politely.

"I am the Christmas Angel," said the lady with a smile. "Who are you, and why are you here?"

"Oh, I live in the house. My babies are asleep in the loft, just above where the children are sleeping," said the spider. "I had never seen a Christmas tree, so when the children talked about the one down here, I wanted to see it for myself. May I look at the tree now?"

"It is the children's tree," said the lady. "Perhaps they wouldn't want you to look at it."

"Dearie me!" said the spider. "The children would want me to see their tree. Why, I work and play close by them every day. I love those six children."

"Well," said the Christmas Angel, "if you have love in your heart, you may look at the children's tree, but you must change nothing."

"The tree is so big, and I am so little," said the spider very wistfully. "I can't see very well. Couldn't I please go up in the tree? I'll be very, very careful."

"If you are very sure that you have love in your heart, and if your feet are surely clean, you may climb the tree, I suppose," said the Christmas Angel. "You must hurry, though, for I am in a hurry, and I must leave everything as I found it."

The mother spider thanked her, and ran quickly up the trunk of the Christmas tree. She went round and round the limbs. She went round and round the packages also. She sniffed some good smells, and smacked her lips on a bit of sugar that she found outside one bag of candy. Last of all, she went to the very tip-top and looked down on the beautiful Christmas tree. Then she ran to the Angel, made another curtsy, and said: "Thank you, Christmas Angel. I wish my babies could have a Christmas tree someday. I shall bring them all down to see it tomorrow." She had started up the ladder to bed, when suddenly the sound of a cross voice frightened her so that she almost fell off the ladder.

"You naughty spider," said the Christmas Angel. "Come right back here. You told me you had love in your heart, and that you would not hurt the children's tree. See what you have done to it! You have covered it with ugly, gray cobwebs. Oh, dear! Oh, dear! What shall I do?"

Tears were falling from the eyes of the mother spider as she came and stood before the Christmas Angel again. Her knees were shaking so that she could hardly stand.

"I do have love in my heart," she said. "I do love the children. I had nothing else to give to the children for their tree. I gave them every bit of web I had, and now I have nothing left with which to make my children a new home tomorrow. I thought the children would like my nice web on their tree. I'm sorry. I'm very sorry. What can we do?"

"There, there!" said the Christmas Angel. "Wipe your eyes. If you gave the web to make the children happy, and because you had love in your heart, then I must do something about it. See! I will wave my wand."

The eyes of the mother spider grew bigger and bigger, for the gray lines on the tree began to change to silver and to gold. They glittered, and shone, and sparkled in the light that came from the shining robe of the Angel. Over the tree, around the packages, and even about the picture of the Christmas Angel on the top of the tree were the beautiful silver and gold trimmings.

"Oh! Oh! How beautiful!" exclaimed the spider. "Thank you so much. Now I can go to bed knowing that I have done something to make the children happy tomorrow. Their tree is much more beautiful than when I saw it first."

"I think that is so," said the Angel. "Good night, little mother spider, and Merry Christmas."

The spider went to bed, and the Angel started on her way, but she looked back as she went through the gate.

" 'Tis the most beautiful tree in many a mile," she said. "I must tell other mothers to trim the children's trees with silver and gold threads, just as the spider has done. Love makes all things beautiful. Love is the greatest gift in the world."

The mothers of the Settlement Mothers' Club sat very still

when the mother from Finland had finished her story. They liked it; they were eager to pass it on to their own children at bedtime. Suddenly one of the mothers touched the Story Lady on the arm, saying: "See! Her story must be true. A mother spider is coming to trim our children's Christmas tree before our very eyes."

Over the tree dangled a long gray cobweb, which was being steadily lengthened. At the end of the line was a spider. She swung for a moment in the breeze from the bright fire in the fireplace; then she dropped into the heart of the Christmas tree. The mothers watched intently for a moment or two, hoping that they could see her spinning a web. When she appeared for a moment on one of the limbs, they clapped enthusiastically for the mother from Finland, for the little spider in the tree, and for the gift of the beautiful story which I have now passed on to you.

FRANCE

The Cobbler and His Guest

ANNE McCOLLUM BOYLES

THERE ONCE LIVED in the city of Marseilles an elderly shoemaker, loved and honored by his neighbors, who affectionately called him "Father Martin."

One Christmas Eve, as he sat alone in his little shop reading of the visit of the Wise Men to the infant Jesus, and of the gifts they brought, he said to himself: "If tomorrow were the first Christmas, and if this Jesus were to be born in Marseilles this night, I know what I would give him!" He rose from his stool and took from a shelf overhead two tiny shoes of softest snow-white leather, with bright silver buckles. "I would give him these, my finest work."

Replacing the shoes, he blew out the candles and retired to rest. Hardly had he closed his eyes, it seemed, when he heard a voice call his name: "Martin! Martin!" Intuitively he felt a Presence. Then the voice spoke again: "Martin, you have wished to see me. Tomorrow I shall pass by your window. If you see me, and bid me enter, I shall be your guest at your table."

Father Martin did not sleep that night for joy, and before it was dawn he rose and swept and tidied up his little shop. He spread fresh sand upon the floor and wreathed green boughs of fir along the rafters. On the spotless, linen-covered table he placed a loaf of white bread, a jar of honey, and a pitcher of milk, and over the fire he hung a pot of tea.

Then he took up his patient vigil at the window.

Presently he saw an old street sweeper pass by, blowing upon his thin, gnarled hands to warm them. "Poor fellow, he must be half frozen," thought Martin. Opening the door, he called out to him, "Come in, my friend, and warm yourself and drink a cup of hot tea." And the man gratefully accepted the invitation.

An hour passed, and Martin saw a young, miserably clothed woman carrying a baby. She paused wearily to rest in the shelter of his doorway. The heart of the old cobbler was touched. Quickly he flung open the door.

"Come in and warm yourself while you rest," he said to her. "You do not look well," he remarked.

"I am going to the hospital. I hope they will take me in and my baby boy," she explained. "My husband is at sea, and I am ill, without a penny."

"Poor child!" cried Father Martin. "You must eat something while you are getting warm. No? Then let me give a cup of milk to the little one. Ah! What a bright, pretty little fellow he is! Why, you have put no shoes on him!"

"I have no shoes for him," sighed the mother sadly.

"Then he shall have this lovely pair I finished yesterday," and Father Martin took down from the shelf the soft little snow-white shoes he had admired the evening before. And shortly the poor young mother left, two small coins in her hand and tearful with gratitude.

And Father Martin resumed his place at the window. Hour after hour went by, and although many people passed his window, and many needy souls shared his hospitality, the expected Guest did not appear.

"It was only a dream," he sighed with a heavy heart. "I did hope and believe, but He has not come."

Suddenly, so it seemed to his weary eyes, the room was flooded with a strange light. And to the cobbler's astonished vision there appeared before him, one by one, the poor street sweeper, the sick mother and her child, and the other people whom he had aided during the day. And each smiled at him and said: "Have you not seen Me? Did I not sit at your table?" Then they vanished.

At last, out of the silence, Father Martin heard again the gentle voice repeating the old familiar words: " 'Whoso shall receive one such little child in my name receiveth me. . . . For

I was ahungered, and ye gave me meat: I was thirsty, and ye gave me drink: I was a stranger, and ye took me in: . . . verily I say unto you, Inasmuch as ye have done it unto one of the least of these my brethren, ye have done it unto me.' "

GERMANY

Annaliese's Christmas Wish

GERTRUDE DOEDERLEIN

SO MUCH SNOW! For days the air had been wet with countless snowflakes that looked like bits of white frosting as they crowded one another for a place to touch and work their magic.

The narrow, cobbled streets were turned into white sugar cushions. The fountain in the marketplace gradually took on the shape of a huge birthday cake. You no more than crossed the street and you looked like a frosted gingerbread man.

It made things really festive—the snow, the time of year, and all. For it was Christmas week. In fact, only one more day remained. This was the last "before" day, and it had almost slipped by.

Darkness came early in December. Streetlights began to blink under their snowy caps. Shop lights in the crooked streets blinked back one by one. Each window seemed to send out a special invitation to come and have your pick of Christmas wares.

Right on the corner was Mr. Kredel's bakery shop. Instead of the usual bread and rolls, the baker and his wife had fashioned the most delightful things out of cookie dough and baked them to a crisp brown. There were trees of all sizes, a whole forest, and in their midst stood a house that glistened with red, green, yellow, and even blue sugar. The house was held together, of all things, with dark-brown chocolate. Its windows were made of strawberry cream.

You knew at once that the house belonged to the old witch from the Ilsenstein. Behind the cookie tree you could see the old witch watching Hansel and Gretel as they came out of the forest. It was something to look at, indeed.

Around the corner near the school, Kasper the butcher had set up a puppet theater. Several children stood in front of it, nudging and laughing with one another while they waited for the performance to begin. When the curtain parted, a huge mountain was seen in the background. From the cave came tiny elves, one after the other, each pushing a wheelbarrow. They carried to children everywhere good things to eat for Christmas, so the storyteller said. Back and forth they trudged, nodding their heads, laughing and making jokes, much to the amusement of the children.

But the largest and most exciting window in the whole town belonged to Mr. Andreas the toy maker, who lived on a little street called Turm Gasse. The window was lined with soft fleecy clouds that seemed to have been lifted right out of the sky especially for this place. Tiny stars sparkled here and there, half hidden in the make-believe clouds. A stairway led from the foot to the top of the window. At the head of it you could see a door painted so invitingly in delicate colors that it made you wonder what might be behind it.

Toys of every kind had been placed on each one of the steps of the stairway. On the bottom stood two curlyheaded dolls with long blue dresses and bags to match. The next step had a row of soldiers, in white uniforms trimmed in red, standing at attention, stiff and straight. Then came a family of bears—father, mother, and baby. Father proudly wore his cap and checkered vest, mother a flower bonnet and apron, baby a red jacket and a green hat with a feather. On the next higher step there were little chairs, tables, beds, boxes, clocks, jumping jacks, chimney sweeps, blocks, and trains. On the very top step, next to the closed door, stood a Christmas tree loaded from its tip to its last branch with shining things—stars, balls, icicles, tiny houses, churches, angels, gilded nuts and apples. The tree went round and round in a silver music box that played "Silent Night! Holy Night!"

Now, the best part of it all was the door. Every now and then it slowly opened, and out came Christkind. Then it closed and Christkind disappeared behind it. The people were crowded in front of the window close as a wall. They pushed and squeezed one another to get a second look at Christkind's lovely smile.

No one saw little Annaliese stand beside the window with her basket filled with red, green, and silver *Tüten*. Was it any wonder when everyone was looking up and Annaliese stood no higher than a fence post? Annaliese's too-small coat was thin and worn. Her head scarf was saturated and sent little melted snowflakes darting after each other down her pale, cold cheeks. Her hands were quite blue and stiff although she tried to keep one in her pocket while she held out her *Tüten* with the other.

Annaliese's Christmas *Tüten* were pretty. She and her mother had made them from scraps of paper, then filled them with lebkuchen. Over the top they had fastened small squares of paper cut into lacy patterns. Annaliese must sell her *Tüten* today because Mother had used her last flour and butter to make them. If she did not sell them, Mother would be sad again; there would not be enough money. Every afternoon Annaliese took her place here by the toy maker's window, hoping that the crowd of gay people would notice her *Tüten*. But the people had eyes only for the window. Even Annaliese could not help taking a look at the beautiful window occasionally. Whenever the door opened and Christkind came out she whispered, "Christkind, please come to my house!"

The snowflakes kept on tossing and twirling as brightly as ever, but the gables of the houses grew dim against the gray-blue evening sky. At St. Georg's church the bells sounded the time—seven o'clock. Mother said Annaliese must leave for home at this time because she had a far way to go, through the tower gate, across the river. It would be quite dark along the narrow road that led to their home at the end of the town.

Annaliese hoped her mother would not be sad tonight. After all, it was Christmas. And Christmas was still the same, full of secret smiles and expectation. The people in the street had been that way, she noticed. Or would Christmas be different too, like everything else at home these days? Things being different had begun way back when the family had to flee and when father was taken away. A new home in the new land was hard to find. Mother had become ill over it. Had it not been for Bauer Hetzel, they probably would have starved. It was he who had given Mother work too. She baked for him. But it was not enough to provide for the two of them, so Annaliese helped by selling lebkuchen. She was making patterns in the snow with her toe as all these grown-up thoughts crossed her mind. Now she had better try once more to sell her *Tüten*.

"Lebkuchen, fine lebkuchen for your Christmas, please buy!" It was no use. No one heard. Her voice was lost in the crowd noises.

Just then she saw Christkind come out from the door. This time Christkind looked directly at Annaliese. She was sure of it. Now she knew. Christkind would not forget to come. She tried to smile back but her face had become too stiff with cold.

She would start for home. Christkind was coming. All the way through the tower gate, across the river, along the narrow road, the thought sustained her. But when she reached home and saw Mother's face her sureness fled. Mother was even sadder than usual. The house was dark except for the little dim lamp on the table. No forbidden closed doors to hide away the mysterious preparations for Christmas Eve.

They sat down to eat the rest of yesterday's potato soup and bread. Mother was quiet and that made Annaliese quiet too. Soon after their meal, when the table was cleared, they went to bed and Mother blew out the lamp. It was just too dark and Annaliese cried herself to sleep. Her last thoughts were of Christkind smiling and nodding to her. Half asleep she murmured, "Come, dearest Christkind!"

Suddenly it seemed as though she were wide awake. With a start she sat bolt upright in her bed and looked about. In the far corner of the next room she saw, to her amazement, a tree glowing with a thousand candles and sparkling with shining things, like the tree in the toy maker's window. It was slowly going round and round in its silver music box playing "Silent Night! Holy Night!"

Little elves came trudging from behind the tree, bringing, of all things, the curlyheaded doll with the long blue dress and bag to match. Some carried good things to eat—nuts, fruits, sweets, even sausages and a ham. They emptied their wheelbarrows under the tree and scampered away as quickly as they had come. Annaliese stared as the door opened and Christkind entered. She called so loudly, "Christkind, Christkind!" that it awakened her, and the beautiful dream vanished.

Mother was at her side the moment she heard the call. "It was only a dream. Even Christkind. Oh, Mother!" Annaliese cried.

Very slowly, as though she were just now remembering it herself, Mother explained that Christkind is never a dream. He is always real. "We will go to Christkind and bring him home with us. You wait and see," said Mother.

"But where?" sobbed Annaliese.

"Church, of course," said Mother.

Both hurried to get into their coats, still damp from the snow. They had barely enough time to reach St. Georg's for the Midnight Service. "Christkind will be there, wait and see," Mother kept reassuring Annaliese.

When they stepped out into the night it seemed more like Christmas again. The air was swept clean by a cold wind. No more snow. Instead there were stars in the sky. The whole countryside was alive with tiny moving lights, like candles on a huge Christmas tree. Tinkling bells and joyous calls interrupted the quiet of the night. Others were going to the Midnight Service too. From the hills and farms they came, carrying lanterns to light the way. Some walked, some rode in sleds or wagons, jingling bells and wishing Christmas blessings as they passed each other.

The old church, though spacious, was crowded to the last pew. Annaliese and her mother had to stand far back. But Annaliese could look down the high, vaulted center aisle to the main altar in its festive snow-white paraments. On the side of the altar stood the figures of Joseph and Mary, bending over the child Jesus in the manger. Shepherds stood near the stable. How poor they looked! But what about Christkind on a bed of straw? Was he not the poorest of them all? Annaliese took comfort from this.

The service began. The pastor fulfilled his duties at the altar. Then came the beloved *Quempas-Singen*, a custom as old as St. Georg's. The boys were divided into four choirs. Each choir sang one line of a song. At the end of each stanza the people, the organ, all the choirs, joined together in a mighty "*In dulci jubilo*."

At first Annaliese tried to see where the singing began, but it soon came to her from all sides. The whole church was filled with the melody and the words:

" 'Come, your hearts and voices raising, Christ the Lord with gladness praising . . .' " " 'Now sing we, now rejoice . . . Thou my Savior art . . .' " " 'Gracious child, we pray thee, hear us . . . Gently lead us and be near us . . .' "

Annaliese looked up at her mother and saw that her face had softened into a smile. She must be happy again the way she used to be. Annaliese sang, " 'Thou my Savior art!' " as she had never sung before. All the things she had been missing—a tree, toys, food—were forgotten, as she was filled with love and joy over Christkind, the Savior. Did she not hold in her heart the only gift that could make you rich and glad—Christkind and his love?

Back at home the same empty darkness greeted Annaliese and her mother. Somehow it was less dark and less cold to Annaliese. You see, Mother was smiling. She quickly tucked the tired child into bed again. It had grown late after the Midnight Service, even though Bauer Hetzel had picked them up at the tower gate and whirled them home in his sled drawn by the two black horses. Annaliese was too tired to think. She just felt better; Christkind was near. Soon she was sound asleep.

It was daylight when Annaliese opened her eyes again. Mother stood by her bed. She was still smiling. "Hurry, get up, little sleepyhead!" she said.

Annaliese noticed something, even though she was barely awake. The door to the next room was closed. Now Mother opened it a bit and Annaliese heard the familiar tinkle of a music box playing "Silent Night! Holy Night!" Carefully, slowly, she looked. Was it really true?

With one leap she was out of bed and at the door. There it

stood—the tree—exactly like the dream, with the music box making it go round and round! Mother helped her dress. She was so excited that she ran to the tree and saw the curlyheaded doll with the long blue dress and bag to match. There were nuts, fruits, sweets, even sausages and a ham. Way under the tree, carefully folded, lay a warm red dress and white apron. Annaliese looked and looked.

"But when?" she wanted to know. "When did Christkind come?" Because children in this part of the world always receive their gifts on Christmas Eve and here it was Christmas morning, Mother explained. "Bauer Hetzel helped Christkind. Last night you were so tired he did not want to disturb you."

"I will give him the bag of nuts and help him every day," said Annaliese gratefully.

She took up the doll and tenderly cradled her in one arm. She took the dress in the other arm, then the fruits, nuts, and sweets, until she could hold no more. "Last night I knew it," she said. "After church I felt it inside of me and now I feel it outside of me too."

"What do you feel?" asked Mother.

"Christkind is really here."

"Yes, and to stay," said Mother, smiling.

The Little Clockmaker

RUTH SAWYER

ONCE UPON A TIME there lived in Germany a little clockmaker by the name of Hermann Joseph. He lived in one little room with a bench for his work, and a chest for his wood, and his tools, and a cupboard for dishes, and a trundle bed under the bench. Besides these there was a stool, and that was all—excepting the clocks. There were hundreds of clocks: little and big, carved and plain, some with wooden faces and some with porcelain ones, shelf clocks, cuckoo clocks, clocks with chimes and clocks without; and they all hung on the walls, covering them entirely. In front of his one little window there was a little shelf, and on this Hermann put all his best clocks to show the passersby. Often they would stop and look and someone would cry: "See, Hermann Joseph has made a new clock. It is finer than any of the rest!"

Then if it happened that anybody was wanting a clock, he would come in and buy it.

I said Hermann was a little clockmaker. That was because his back was bent and his legs were crooked, which made him very short and funny to look at. But there was no kinder face than his in all the city, and the children loved him. Whenever a toy was broken or a doll had lost an arm or a leg or an eye, its careless *Mütterchen* would carry it straight to Hermann's little shop.

"The *Kindlein* needs mending," she would say. "Canst thou do it now for me?"

And whatever work Hermann was doing, he would always put it aside to mend the broken toy or doll, and never a *Pfennig* would he take for the mending.

"Go spend it for sweetmeats, or, better still, put it by till Christmastime. 'Twill get thee some happiness then, maybe," he would always say.

Now it was the custom in that long ago for those who lived in the city to bring gifts to the great cathedral on Christmas and lay them before the Holy Mother and Child. People saved all through the year that they might have something wonderful to bring on that day; and there was a saying among them that when a gift was brought that pleased the Christ-child more than any other he would reach down from Mary's arms and take it. This was but a saying, of course. The old Herr Graff, the oldest man in the city, could not remember that it had ever really happened; and many there were who laughed at the very idea. But children often talked about it, and the poets made beautiful verses about it; and often, when a rich gift was placed beside the altar, the watchers would whisper among themselves, "Perhaps now we shall see the miracle."

Those who had no gifts to bring went to the cathedral just

the same on Christmas Eve to see the gifts of the others and hear the carols and watch the burning of the waxen tapers. The little clockmaker was one of these. Often he was stopped and someone would ask, "How happens it that you never bring a gift?" Once the bishop himself questioned him: "Poorer than thou have brought offerings to the Child. Where is thy gift?"

Then it was that Hermann had answered: "Wait; someday you shall see. I too shall bring a gift someday."

The truth of it was that the little clockmaker was so busy giving away all the year that there was never anything left at Christmastime. But he had a wonderful idea on which he was working every minute that he could spare time from his clocks. It had taken him years and years; no one knew anything about it but Trude, his neighbor's child, and Trude had grown from a baby into a little housemother, and still the gift was not finished.

It was to be a clock, the most wonderful and beautiful clock ever made; and every part of it had been fashioned with loving care. The case, the works, the weights, the hands, and the face, all had taken years of labor. He had spent years carving the case and hands, years perfecting the works; and now Hermann saw that with a little more haste and time he could finish it for the coming Christmas. He mended the children's toys as before, but he gave up making his regular clocks, so there were fewer to sell, and often his cupboard was empty and he went supperless to bed. But that only made him a little thinner and his face a little kinder; and meantime the gift clock became more and more beautiful. It was fashioned after a rude stable, with rafters, stall, and crib. The Holy Mother knelt beside the manger in which a tiny Christ-child lay, while through the open door the hours came. Three were kings and three were shepherds and three were soldiers and three were angels; and when the hour struck, the figure knelt in adoration before the sleeping Child, while the silver chimes played the *Magnificat*.

"Thou seest," said the clockmaker to Trude, "it is not just on Sundays and holidays that we should remember to worship the Krist Kindlein and bring him gifts—but every day, every hour."

The days went by like clouds scudding before a winter wind and the clock was finished at last. So happy was Hermann with his work that he put the gift clock on the shelf before the little window to show the passersby. There were crowds looking at it all day long, and many would whisper, "Do you think this can be the gift Hermann has spoken of—his offering on Christmas Eve to the church?"

The day before Christmas came. Hermann cleaned up his little shop, wound all his clocks, brushed his clothes, and then went over the gift clock again to be sure everything was perfect.

"It will not look meanly beside the other gifts," he thought happily. In fact, he was so happy that he gave away all but one *Pfennig* to the blind beggar who passed his door; and then, remembering that he had eaten nothing since breakfast, he spent that last *Pfennig* for a Christmas apple to eat with a crust of bread he had. These he was putting by in the cupboard to eat after he was dressed, when the door opened and Trude was standing there crying softly.

"*Kindlein*, *Kindlein*, what ails thee?" And he gathered her into his arms.

" 'Tis the father. He is hurt, and all the money that was put by for the tree and sweets and toys has gone to the Herr Doktor. And now, how can I tell the children? Already they have lighted the candle at the window and are waiting for Kriss Kringle to come."

The clockmaker laughed merrily.

"Come, come, little one, all will be well. Hermann will sell a clock for thee. Some house in the city must need a clock; and in a wink we shall have money enough for the tree and the toys. Go home and sing."

He buttoned on his greatcoat, and picking out the best of the old clocks, he went out. He went first to the rich merchants, but their houses were full of clocks; then to the journeymen, but they said his clock was old-fashioned. He even stood on the corners of the streets and in the square, crying, "A clock, a good clock for sale," but no one paid any attention to him. At last he gathered up his courage and went to the Herr Graff himself.

"Will Your Excellency buy a clock?" he said, trembling at his own boldness. "I would not ask, but it is Christmas, and I am needing to buy happiness for some children."

The Herr Graff smiled.

"Yes, I will buy a clock, but not that one. I will pay a thousand *Gulden* for the clock thou hast had in thy window these four days past."

"But, Your Excellency, that is impossible!" And poor Hermann trembled harder than ever.

"Poof! Nothing is impossible. That clock or none. Get thee home, and I will send for it in half an hour and pay thee the *Gulden*."

The little clockmaker stumbled out.

"Anything but that, anything but that!" he kept mumbling over and over to himself on his way home. But as he passed the neighbor's house he saw the children at the window with their lighted candle and he heard Trude singing.

And so it happened that the servant who came from the Herr Graff carried the gift clock away with him; but the clockmaker would take but five of the thousand *Gulden* in payment. And as the servant disappeared up the street the chimes commenced to ring from the great cathedral, and the streets suddenly became noisy with the many people going thither, bearing their Christmas offerings.

"I have gone empty-handed before," said the little clockmaker sadly. "I can go empty-handed once again." And again he buttoned up his greatcoat.

As he turned to shut his cupboard door behind him, his eyes fell on the Christmas apple, and an odd little smile crept into the corners of his mouth and lighted his eyes.

"It is all I have—my dinner for two days. I will carry that to the Christ-child. It is better, after all, than going empty-handed."

How full of peace and beauty was the great cathedral when Hermann entered it! There were a thousand tapers burning, and everywhere the sweet scent of the Christmas greens—and the laden altar before the Holy Mother and Child. There were richer gifts than had been brought for many years: marvelously wrought vessels from the greatest silversmiths; cloth of gold and cloth of silk brought from the East by the merchants; poets had brought their songs illuminated on rolls of heavy parchment; painters had brought their pictures of saints and the Holy Family; even the king himself had brought his crown and scepter to lay before the Child. And after all these offerings came the little clockmaker, walking slowly down the long, dim aisle, holding tight to his Christmas apple.

The people saw him, and a murmur rose, hummed a moment indistinctly through the church, and then grew clear and articulate: "Shame! See, he is too mean to bring his clock! He hoards it as a miser hoards his gold. See what he brings! Shame!"

The words reached Hermann, and he stumbled on blindly, his head dropped forward on his breast, his hands groping the way. The distance seemed interminable. Now he knew he was past the seats; now his feet touched the first step, and there were seven to climb to the altar. Would his feet never reach the top?

"One, two, three," he counted to himself, then tripped and almost fell. "Four, five, six." He was nearly there. There was but one more.

The murmur of shame died away and in its place rose one of wonder and awe. Soon the words became intelligible: "The miracle! It is the miracle!"

The people knelt in the big cathedral; the bishop raised his hands in prayer. And the little clockmaker, stumbling to the last step, looked up through dim eyes and saw the Child leaning toward him, far down from Mary's arms, with hands outstretched to take his gift.

HOLLAND

The Smiling Lady

MARGARET W. EGGLESTON

IT HAD BEEN ten long days since the lady with the smiling face had come upon the group of Dutch children in the village park far across the sea. Perhaps she had been near them for a long time, had listened to their talk of shepherds, and Wise Men, and angels, and of the Holy Babe. It may be that she had heard them tell each other of the gifts they would have brought to Mary and the Christ-child. She might have been hidden from them by the great tree trunk that was just across the tiny brook from where the children were sitting. The children didn't know, and didn't care. Neither do I.

When the children first saw the Smiling Lady, as they soon called her, she was asking Trudy to come across the brook and talk to her. They saw then that her face was kind and loving, and they urged Trudy to go. Later on, she had told them wonderful stories of the first Christmas, and they had sung their Christmas carols to her. When the time had come to leave the park, she had told them that if they would come alone to the same place on Christmas Eve, at eight o'clock, she was sure they could see Mary and Joseph and the Babe. Perhaps they might even hear the angels' song.

The children didn't know her name, nor where she lived. Emil thought she must have come from over the sea. Wilhelmina was sure that she must be rich, for her clothes were fine and beautiful. Griselda said she knew they could trust her, for she looked like a good mother.

Aunts and cousins smiled as they heard the children make their plans for Christmas Eve, based on the things the Smiling

Lady had told them, but the mothers of the children wondered who this woman might be who dared to promise such a treat to the little ones. Was it safe to let them go alone with Emil after twilight had fallen?

Soon the children had chosen a little Christmas tree. This was to be lighted with candles—one for each child—and it was to be placed, first of all their gifts, before the Holy Babe. Hetty, whom they all loved because she was never mean and cross, was to carry it. Fritz had determined that he too would have a tree. As he had no money with which to buy candles, he had invited Katrina and Ferdinand to share it with him, and to help to secure red and yellow things with which to trim it.

Wilhelmina had pressed her blue ribbons carefully, for she was proud of her long braids, and she wanted to look her best. Hendrik had hunted long for a sturdy basket that might hold the good things which Emil and Mark and Fritz and he were hoping to carry to the Mother and Babe from the garden which the boys had been making. Hendrik wasn't at all sure that he could blow his horn and carry a heavy basket at the same time, but he wanted much to try, for the Babe would like the sound of his horn, he knew.

Dear little Trudy, the pet of the village, was preparing to make the biggest sacrifice of all. The Smiling Lady had told her that the shepherds brought a young lamb to the Babe—a spotless lamb, the finest of the flock. Now, Trudy had a lamb, and it was her dearest treasure. It was blue in color, and it ran on small wheels. She was going to take her lamb to the park when she went on Christmas Eve, she said, for she felt sure that the Babe would like a lamb better than a tree with candles.

Ten days! How slowly they go when children wait their passing! When eight days had gone, dresses were clean, coats had been pressed, shoes were ready, carols had been practiced over and over, and gifts had been put in a special place. The children were talking of nothing but shepherds and wise men, camels and angels, the Mother and the Child.

At last the great day had come, and twilight had fallen. One by one the children met at the appointed place. Rabbits were still hopping about. A mother deer and her fawn—friends of the children because of their habit of feeding them—were browsing under the trees. A bird sang an evening song from the limb of an oak, and another bird, with wings of blue, was taking a final drink from the brook when the children came.

As the village clock chimed the quarter-hour the children formed into line, often looking back to see if Hendrik and Gretchen had yet come to join them. Where could they be? How sweet and clean the children all looked in their quaint Dutch costumes! With what awe they peered across the brook to the place where the Smiling Lady had told them they might see the Holy Family.

Hetty walked first, very proud of the fact that she was the bearer of the lighted tree. Her yellow hair was braided at the sides and tied with blue ribbons. Her dark-blue dress had flowers of blue and violet scattered over it. Hetty remembered, as she walked, that she must let no candle drip on this, her Sunday dress. The candles on her Christmas tree sent their light across the brook toward the great tree. Fifteen candles on a little tree; fifteen Dutch children following the tree. That is what two little rabbits saw.

Behind Hetty walked Fritz, his small feet trying hard to keep pace with the rest. His straight white hair was covered with a cheery cap of red; his chubby legs were gay with striped stockings, his pride and joy. Fritz didn't like the woods at night, so he kept close to sister, as he carried his own pretty Christmas tree; its apples, and toys, and cards, all love gifts from boys to a baby boy.

Griselda pressed close behind, holding Anne very tight, lest she be afraid. She pointed to the beautiful tree as they waited, and bade Anne watch the flickering lights. Griselda wore a green skirt, a blue apron, a speckled waist, and her gray hood. Little Anne was quaint and dear in her new gray dress, with a lavender hood pulled tightly under her chin and a speckled handkerchief tied about her neck.

Wilhelmina came next, her braided hair tied with her neat blue ribbons. A blue apron covered her dress. Close beside her walked young Hans. Wilhelmina had promised her mother to take good care of him, so she tried to make him happy by telling him of all the wonderful things they were going to see and hear. His dark eyes were big with wonder, and he could hardly wait for the time to pass.

Hanging tight to Griselda's apron was Trudy—dear, little chubby Trudy. In her right hand she held the string that led to the blue lamb, which was trailing along behind her. Her dress of red and blue plaid was covered with a tight-fitting coat of bright red, and her cute bonnet was closely tied under her fat chin. Griselda, while caring tenderly for Anne, still watched over Trudy as she marched along with the rest. Surely the Holy Babe would love little Trudy when she knelt to place the blue lamb in his hands.

Right in the center of the group, Mark rode on the young fawn. Emil had lifted him to its back, and had slipped some red reins over the head of the fawn to guide it. With one hand he carefully steadied young Mark; with the other he held the reins lest the fawn try to break away. Emil was the oldest boy of the group, and he dreamed of the day when he might be like that other Hans of the dike lands—a hero. He talked to Mark of the Mother and Babe as they stood in the gathering dusk, while Julius, just behind, tried hard to hear what was being said. Julius knew well what fine stories Emil could tell.

Gretel, never able to keep still for long, was already singing, very quietly, one of their carols, while Katrina and Ferdinand, their minds full of wise men and camels, kept far in the rear to see that no little one lagged behind.

Hendrik and Gretchen were late. Hendrik's basket and horn had been ready since morning, but Gretchen was to bring the beautiful blue lilies that were growing in her mother's garden. Lilies to be given to the Holy Mother must be fresh and sweet, so Gretchen had waited as long as possible before picking them. Doll in arm, she joined Hendrik, whose anxiety lest they should not get to their place before the appointed hour made him hurry along as fast as he could.

"Do you suppose Mary loves her Babe as I do mine?" Gretchen asked. "Will she be glad to see my baby doll?" Hendrik had no time to answer. Soon they had joined the children near the brook.

Fifteen small children, all of whom had come together on the word of a stranger. Would they be disappointed? Emil wondered. The rest were full of expectation. The stars were peeping through the dark of the sky and all was still. The children held their breaths as the village clock chimed the hour—one-two-three-four-five-six-seven-eight. It was the hour set by their friend. They were there and ready, so they sang quietly:

> " 'O come to my heart, Lord Jesus,
> There is room in my heart for thee.' "

A bright star then shone in the sky over the great tree, and its yellow light streamed through the leaves down to a spot right under the spreading branches, just across the brook from Hetty. The evening song of the bird ceased. The mother deer lifted her head, but seemed unafraid. Two little rabbits stood on their hind legs right in front of Hetty, eager to see why the light had come again. The tiny spruce tree near the brook, looking like another Christmas tree, was bathed in light and was very beautiful. Thrilled and awed, the children waited in silence.

Under the great tree, dressed in shining white, there appeared a beautiful mother with a dazzling blue drapery over her head. In her arms lay a wondrous babe with smiling face and yellow hair. Behind the two stood a tall, strong, happy man, bending proudly over his family. Before them knelt shepherds, leaning on their staffs. Behind the shepherds were four golden-haired angels—tiny ones—and they sang:

> " 'O come, let us adore him;
> O come, let us adore him;
> O come, let us adore him, Christ, the Lord.' "

"The mother is like the Smiling Lady, only she is more beautiful," said Griselda to herself.

"The baby has yellow hair like mine," thought Trudy. "I hope he will smile when I give him my lamb."

"There is a young shepherd, no older than myself," whispered Emil to Mark. "I wish I might have been a shepherd then, and have gone to worship him."

While the children stood awed, reverent, thrilled, the light slowly faded, the song of the angels ceased, and then the park was dark, save for the candles on Hetty's tree.

"Oh!" cried Trudy. "He hasn't taken the lamb!"

"I have lilies for Mary. I want to give them to her," said Gretchen, ready to cry with disappointment.

"Where has the Babe gone? I want to see the Babe again," called Mark.

"Come, children," said wise Emil, stepping to the front of the line and lifting Mark to his arms. "Don't you remember that the Smiling Lady told us that we should see Mary and Joseph and the Babe, but that we could not speak to them? Let us leave our gifts here, now that we have seen the Holy Family with our own eyes. Let us trust the Smiling Lady that Mary will be happy with what we have brought, and that she and the Babe will take them to children who are sick and lonely and unhappy."

"I'll put my tree down right here by the pretty spruce that was in the yellow light," said Hetty.

"And mine shall be close by," said Fritz.

So the lamb, and the basket of good things, and the blue lilies were all laid under the three Christmas trees. When Emil raised his hand, the Dutch children began to sing, as they had promised to do:

> " 'O come, all ye faithful,
> Joyful and triumphant;
> O come ye, O come ye to Bethlehem;
> Come and behold him, born the King of angels;
> O come, let us adore him;
> O come, let us adore him;
> O come, let us adore him, Christ, the Lord.' "

The voices of the angels had been sweet, but sweeter far were the voices of the Dutch children as they slowly went back to their homes, singing as they went. The deer, the birds, the rabbits, had all gone to rest. Nothing but the carols of the children broke the stillness of that Christmas Eve.

"Weren't they dear?" asked a sweet voice from the darkness under the great tree, when every little child had disappeared.

"Not more dear than you were to bring them such a wonderful Christmas treat," answered a man's deep voice. "They will never forget this Christmas Eve."

"Nor shall I," was the reply, as she bent to kiss her child before handing him to the father to carry. "Someday we shall tell little son of this wonderful Christmas in Holland, his very first Christmas Eve."

INDIA

Come to Christmas

JESSIE ELEANOR MOORE

IT WAS Christmas at the boarding school at Madura Mission. Never had Karuna seen anything so lovely as the schoolroom. A single tall candle stood outlined against green palm branches. On the table, where the candle gave its light, was a stable scene with a sheep and a donkey, sweet-faced Mary, Joseph, and the Christmas Baby in a manger. Karuna sat and looked and looked.

The Christmas carols were sung, and the Christmas story was told. Karuna kept her eyes on the little scene before her. She was half afraid it would not be there if she looked away for one moment.

"These are Christmas gifts," said the teacher, and she began to give out bright-colored cloth bags, one to every little girl.

Karuna had never had a Christmas gift. Indeed, she had nothing that was really her own except her sari. When she received her bag, she held it for a long time before she even thought of looking inside.

It was not until after the tall candle that lighted the manger scene had been blown out that she looked into her bag. Slowly she pulled the drawstring and reached in. A hard, square package that smelled sweet—a cake of soap—was the first thing she found. A bag of candies was pulled out next. Something that jingled when she touched it came last—a ring of shining safety pins.

One by one, Karuna laid them on the bench beside her. How pretty! How sweet-smelling! And they were all hers.

She did not even see her father when he came and stood

beside her. School was over for a few days. Now for the long walk home!

When Karuna had thought about home early that morning, she had wished that there was to be no vacation. School was a wonderful place. The days at home would be dull and uninteresting. But now when Karuna saw her father, she remembered her friends in the village. Not one of the little girls had anything that was her own. Not one of them had ever celebrated Christmas. Not one of them had even been to school.

She said good-by to the teacher and skipped away at her father's side. Her gay red bag swung in her hand. She already knew what was going to happen to that bag when she reached her own village.

"Come to Christmas!" called Karuna as soon as she reached home. The neighbor children came. The first ones came slowly, as if half afraid. Karuna had been to school. That made her very important. They peeked around the corner of the house at Karuna waiting for them.

But some of them had noticed the red bag. They had never seen anything so pretty. What could be in it? They gathered around Karuna, and each touched the bag with one finger.

How many little girls there were! Karuna looked at them and then at her gay bag and thought of the few things inside. Then she began to talk. She was telling them about the tall candle, the little manger scene, and the carols. She told the Christmas story.

"There is a Christmas present for everyone," Karuna ended. "A Christmas present is given in love. I give you a part of my school because I love it so."

Then she opened the bag. The safety pins came off the ring. One to each little girl. The candies came out of their paper bag. One to each little girl. And for her best friend, Loti, the sweet-smelling cake of soap. Karuna swung the empty bag by the string.

"You gave us all!" they cried.

"I have the bag," answered Karuna, "and besides, in my school they teach us that Christmas is a special time to 'love one another.' "

And every little girl who had never before had a gift was very eager to go to the school of "love one another."

The Lights of Christmas

ELIZABETH ALLSTROM

THERE WERE neither clocks nor calendars in the small village in India where Jaswunt lived. It did not matter much because he did not need them. The sun told him when to get up and when to go to bed. He knew it was spring when he helped Father plant the seeds and autumn when he helped harvest the grain and store it at home in clay jars.

And Jaswunt knew when it was Christmas! Because then he and Father made preparations together for the coming of the Great Day.

As Christmas drew near, Father would say, "It's time now for us to go to the potter's for new clay saucers for the Christmas lights." Later they would go to the market ten miles away and buy silver squares for icing the Christmas cakes, colored paper for Christmas decorations, and powder to make paints for Mother's Christmas pictures.

On the day before the Great Day, the minister, Padre Sahib, would come from the village beyond and meet the children under the mango tree. Father always came too, and listened with Jaswunt to the story of the baby Jesus and sang with him the shepherds' song.

But this year as Christmas came closer, things were different. Very different!

Father was not at home, and seven-year-old Jaswunt was worried. This year after grain harvest, Father had said, "I'm going to the city to find work in the mill."

When Jaswunt asked, "How can I get ready for Christmas without you?" Father had promised: "I'll be home in time. I'll bring money for the hundred Christmas lights. I'll bring money for everything!"

Father had put his bundle on his back and started on the long walk to the market town where he took the train to the distant city.

Now Christmas would soon be here. Jaswunt knew it was time to get ready for it, but Mother said: "We must wait for Father. What can we do when we have no money?"

One morning Jaswunt told his mother: "Ram Singh says his uncle is going to market to sell his new cart wheels. Please let me ride with him."

Mother consented. "If you are careful, you may go."

Before they left, Jaswunt helped to lift the new wheels into the cart. After the oxen were hitched into place, he and Ram Singh's uncle climbed up for their long ride.

At the market Jaswunt helped to unload the wheels and to set them around the stall for buyers to examine. Afterward he wandered from one booth to another. In one he spied the squares of silver and the colored paper and powder to make the paints.

"If only Father were here, we could buy them now," he thought. In his own pocket there was not one anna—only the roasted lentils Mother had put there for his lunch. How could he ever make ready for Christmas all by himself?

Jaswunt found a shady place and ate his lunch. Soon he saw Ram Singh's uncle on the cart. It must be time to start home!

Jaswunt hopped onto the cart. Ram Singh's uncle seemed in no hurry but said, "Hold out your hands." Into Jaswunt's open palms he dropped some coins. "I sold my wheels and made a fair profit. These are for you. You earned them helping me."

Jaswunt looked at the coins a moment, and his fingers closed quickly over them.

"Oh, thank you!" he cried, and in a flash he was on his way to the booth where he had seen the colored powder. He handed the coins to the man there. "Please give me as many colors as these will buy! Now my mother can paint the pictures for the Great Day!"

At home, Jaswunt handed the package to Mother. "We do not need to wait for Father. I can plan for Christmas."

That evening a knock came at the gate. Jaswunt rushed to answer it. Perhaps it was Father. But no! Father would walk right in!

Outside stood the son of the village headman. He had a letter for Mother. "The mail carrier came through the village about a week ago and left this for you, but my father has been too busy to send it until now."

Mother told Jaswunt: "Tomorrow you will take the letter to Padre Sahib. He will read it for us and tell us what Father says."

It was early when Jaswunt started across the fields to the minister's home in the village beyond.

"Your letter brings good news," Padre Sahib said after reading it. "Your father is in good health. He will come home the day before the Great Day. He says you are to go ahead with the Christmas plans."

"How long before my father comes?" Jaswunt asked.

"The sun will set twice," Padre Sahib told him.

When Mother heard, she said: "I will begin the Christmas paintings tomorrow. At least, they will be ready."

Jaswunt begged: "Let me try to get the lights, Mother. I'll go to the potter's tomorrow."

At the potter's shop Jaswunt almost sang his words. "One hundred clay saucers for our Christmas lights! Father said one hundred!"

The potter turned angrily from his wheel. "Why do you come so late? The Great Day is almost here. I have much work to do. Where is your money?"

Jaswunt explained, "When my father comes from the city for the Great Day, he will pay you."

The potter was not pleased. "Pay me now," he demanded crossly.

Jaswunt could not speak for disappointment. He turned to leave. The potter suddenly pointed to some chipped and uneven saucers. "Take those. They are of no use to me. You may have them without paying."

Jaswunt lifted the saucers carefully and carried them to his courtyard at home. He found that there were fifty.

Next he went to the oil presser and asked for oil. The oil presser patted his head. "My lad, it would not be Christmas without plenty of oil for your lights. You may have some. Your father will pay. I do not worry."

He put Jaswunt's empty jar under the opening in the press and let oil drip slowly into it.

At home again, Jaswunt put the oil beside the saucers. He hurried to the cotton field. The farmer told him: "Take only as much as you need. Such a small amount I gladly give you."

Jaswunt bent over the white snowballs popping from their thick brown pods and picked a little from one and from another, until he had a double handful of the fluffy fibers.

Jaswunt reached home and found Ram Singh waiting with colored paper sheets. "Your court must have waving pennants," Ram Singh said. He stayed and helped Jaswunt cut the paper into pretty shapes. Together they pasted them to long strings and hung them across the courtyard.

Jaswunt called to Mother: "See! They're waving a welcome to Father."

Mother answered, "The paintings on the floor and walls will welcome him, too."

The boys came and stood beside the white design Mother had made on the ground in front of the door. On the wall there was a star and a manger. They watched as Mother added the pictures of the Wise Men riding on their camels.

The next morning, Jaswunt put on clean white pants. Mother brought her wedding scarf from the tin box in honor of Father's return.

But still Father did not come.

In the afternoon Jaswunt went to the mango tree. He listened to the minister tell the story of the baby Jesus, and he sang the shepherd's song:

" 'In the skies on that dark night
The shepherds saw the shining light
And found the Babe all wrapped in white.' "

Still Father did not come.

Toward evening Jaswunt went many times to look out the gate. Each time he told Mother, "Surely Father will be here to help fill the lamps."

When Father did not come, Jaswunt poured the oil into the fifty saucers, rolled the long cotton wicks for them, climbed along the roof, the gate, the courtyard wall, and set the lamps in place ready to light.

At sunset the smoke from many fires cooking the evening meal rose over the village. The lumbering buffaloes, the clumsy cows, the scuffling feet of children, the oxen's bells, sounded along the narrow paths and cart tracks. Every creature moved slowly to its home for the night, but Father did not come.

Jaswunt heard the gay voices of Ram Singh and his other friends as they scrambled along the roofs of their houses and on tops of gates and walls to light their many lamps. He could wait no longer. He climbed from wall to roof and lighted his lamps too.

Again he went to the gate. Again he looked far down the lighted path. In the distance a tall figure turned into the village from the country road. It was Father!

Jaswunt ran to meet him. "Oh, Father, I'm glad you have come!"

Father's big hand closed tightly around Jaswunt's small one, and together they walked home to Mother.

"There were no carts along the road today to give me a ride, so I walked all the way," Father told them. "When night came, it was hard to follow the path. Suddenly, through the darkness, I saw the lamps. The lights of Christmas guided me home."

Father looked at all the signs of Christmas. From his bundles he took the silver squares and the money he had promised and a comb for Mother's hair and a new cap for Jaswunt.

Jaswunt smiled at Father. "You are home! Now we are ready for the Great Day!"

ITALY

Ciro's Bigger World

ALICE GEER KELSEY

CIRO'S WORLD was very small. It consisted of bomb-wrecked houses and rubble-built huts where families who could not pay rent had lived since the war. It was bounded on one side by the beautiful Bay of Naples and on the other side by new apartment houses for families whose fathers had regular work.

Cars, going he knew not where, whizzed past Ciro's scarred door. Ships entered the harbor from somewhere, then puffed away till their wisp of black smoke disappeared where blue sky and blue sea seemed to meet. Ciro often looked up to watch a plane speeding away beyond where eye could see. He never wondered about the unknown travelers or the places they were going. That is, he never wondered till the day he walked to meet music.

Like every child of Naples, Ciro had music within him that no amount of dirt or hunger or crowding could quiet. So when he heard children singing a new song, "*Notte Benigna*," he walked to find them. He stood with them, looking up at a brightly trimmed fir tree on the small balcony of a building that was once a warehouse. If he had had clothes good enough for school, Ciro would have known that the words spelled in lights under the tree were *Casa Mia*, Italian for "my home." It was the children who told him what the words meant.

"We have games and school and clinic," said Anna.

"And something to eat every day," said Vittorio.

"And packages from America," said Dinacci.

"And friends," said Carmellina.

Humming the new tune, Ciro followed them inside the settlement house. A smiling woman named Miss Rosa welcomed him. "You may watch the boys and girls your age rehearse their Christmas play."

She gave him a place to sit in the back corner of a big room full of black-smocked boys and girls.

Sitting there the next few mornings, Ciro discovered whom each child represented in their play *The International Christmas Tree*. Pasquale, one of the bigger boys, was Santa Claus, *Papa Natale* to the Italian children. Luisa, Guiseppe, Maria, Salvatore, Nicola, and their friends were playing that each was a child from a different place, from countries called Spain, Holland, Japan, Sweden, Africa, and other names. Vittorio alone was acting the Italian boy he really was. He turned a big ball of blue and other colors, a "globe of the world" they called it.

At first, Turkey, Switzerland, England, and China were only words to Ciro. Watching the rehearsals and listening to Miss Rosa, he learned that these words stood for places where children lived and worked and played games and watched for Papa Natale. Ciro learned that in all these countries boys and girls were singing "*Notte Benigna*," though they pronounced it differently: "*Stille Nacht*" in Germany, "*Noche de Paz*" in Spain, "*Silent Night*" in England and America. Ciro learned that the globe in Vittorio's hands showed where these places were in relation to one another. But these faraway lands seemed only a dream to a boy who lived in a rubble-built hut and sat in the back corner of the room at Casa Mia to watch and to listen.

"We must find a part for Ciro," Miss Rosa would say. But the teachers were all so busy with their Christmas preparations, which included making round-the-world costumes from the least useful clothes that came in the big burlap bales from America. There was no time to think up a new part for Ciro.

"At least you can be an usher," Miss Rosa promised. But she had not reckoned with the United States Navy!

On the day before the program, fifty children of Casa Mia rode to the shore in navy trucks and then boarded the U.S.S.

Chloris for a Christmas party. There are no better hosts in all the world than one hundred sailors who are a bit homesick for their own children, their smaller brothers and sisters, or nephews and nieces. A doll for every girl! A big ball for every boy! Soap, candy, and a can of orange juice for every child! Games! Songs! And such food!

Most of the children carried their extra food home. Dinacci asked permission to take his turkey bone home to his brother. Anna and Pasquale carried their paper cups of candy and nuts home to their grandparents. Carmellina, who had never had much experience with ice cream, tucked her full paper cup in the corner of her doll box to carry it home to her sister.

But Vittorio just ate and ate and ate. Whenever the sailors offered him more food, he smiled and said, "*Sì*," which is Italian for "Yes." He said, "*Sì*," to more turkey, more ice cream, more candy.

The next day when Ciro sat in his corner watching the children put on their costumes for the play, everyone was there but Vittorio. Luisa became a Spanish girl in a bright full skirt. Guiseppe became a Swiss boy wearing a felt hat with a feather in it. Salvatore became a Japanese boy in a bright kimono. Pasquale became Papa Natale with stuffed-out stomach inside some red pajamas.

The clock ticked nearer to the time for the entertainment. Guests were arriving in the big room next to them. But still the globe of the world waited for Vittorio.

"He has a stomachache," explained Maria, peeking out from her Eskimo hood. She knew because her family shared a room with Vittorio's family. "He ate too much at the sailors' party yesterday."

Then the teachers and the children all waved their hands and talked at once. It was Miss Rosa who first noticed Ciro. He had taken a step forward from his corner, then stopped, wondering how bold he dared be.

"Do you know Vittorio's lines, Ciro?" Miss Rosa asked.

"I know them," answered Ciro's shy, eager voice.

"Do you know what he does in the play?" she asked.

"I know." Ciro was close beside the teachers, his hands

clasped behind his back to keep them from reaching out for the globe.

They heard more footsteps and many voices in the big room. Mothers, fathers, grandparents, sisters, brothers, and neighbors had arrived for the program.

"I know you can do it." Miss Rosa put the globe in Ciro's hands. She hurried him into the pajamas which Vittorio was supposed to be wearing. "Now you look ready for bed on Christmas Eve."

The next room was suddenly quiet. Then there was music. The white-smocked kindergarten children were singing "Away in a Manger," as only children of Naples can sing.

The song ended. Globe in hand, Ciro entered the room full of guests. He walked across the stage, yawned as he had seen Vittorio yawn, and sat down on the bed that had been placed near a gift-filled Christmas tree. Then he began to wonder aloud, as he had heard Vittorio.

"Papa Natale will be coming soon." Ciro slowly turned the globe. "I wonder how the rest of the world celebrates Christmas?"

The lights twinkled. Ciro studied the globe. There was the tap-tap of wooden shoes. Anna, in white cap and apron, walked toward him.

"Shall I tell you about Christmas in Holland?" she asked.

"Please." Ciro held the globe toward Anna, who pointed at the small pink spot that was Holland.

"We call Papa Natale 'Saint Nicholas,' " she said. He comes riding on Saint Nicholas' Eve. We leave our wooden shoes filled with hay to feed his big white horse. In the morning we find gifts in place of the hay."

One by one the costumed children entered. Luisa told how the three kings rode their camels through Spain and left gifts. Guiseppe explained how carefully Swiss men carved wooden crèche figures to tell the story of Jesus' birth. Andrea remembered how sweet the homes of Sweden smelled with freshly cut Christmas pines on either side of the door and juniper branches spread on the floor. Fabio described Germany's Christmas trees and sugar-decorated, toy-shaped ginger cakes. Guido told how choirboys sang Christmas carols in the English churches. Lorenzo described Christmas pageants and "white gifts" of unknown children in American churches. The globe in Ciro's hand suddenly stood for something big and alive.

Then Papa Natale dashed on the stage. It was hard to believe that he was only Pasquale as he began taking little bags of candy from the tree for the children. Ciro waited for Papa Natale's last words, the part of the play he liked best: "You children are all equal in all parts of the world. You speak different languages. You live in homes built in different ways. You have different customs. But you can all live together happily. All of you are God's children."

"*Notte Benigna*," sung by the first-graders, made happy music in Ciro's mind as he walked from Casa Mia toward his wretched piece of a house. He knew that children all over his newly discovered world were glad because a very special baby had been born on that *notte benigna* so long ago.

A car whizzed by. Ciro, walking in its dust, wondered if it was going to Switzerland or France, where there were children so much like him. A motor pounded overhead. Ciro looked up. Perhaps the plane was carrying fathers to be with their children at Christmastime in Greece or Japan. A ship was steaming out of the beautiful Bay of Naples. Ciro watched till there was only a wisp of black smoke where blue sky seemed to meet blue sea. Was the ship going to Africa or Spain or America? Wherever it went, there would be children who played games, watched for Papa Natale, and sang "*Notte Benigna*" in their own language.

Ciro's world had grown very large. He knew, surely, that it was full of God's children, who were ever so much like him.

THE PHILIPPINES

Christmas in the Philippines

ESTHER WOOD

PEDRO and the three girls could hardly wait for Christmas. The little nipa house, with its new roof, was to be a Christmas surprise for Grandmother Paz.

Pedro built a chicken coop, and Aunt Valentina said she would give him two of her chickens to put in it. Uncle Manuel hollowed out the trunk of a bamboo tree for a water bucket. Marciana and Juana scrubbed the little stove until it looked almost new.

When everything was ready, they wrote a letter to Grandmother Paz and asked her to come to visit them for Christmas. They didn't say a word about the little house. They only asked her to bring her sleeping mat and her mosquito net. Pedro asked her to bring something for him, but he wouldn't tell anyone what it was. He wanted it very much, he said.

At last the day came when Uncle Manuel was to bring her from Manila in the carabao cart. He would get back in time for Christmas Eve, he said as he left.

Pedro put a banana tree by the gate and tied it to the fence post. Then he helped the three girls trim it with lanterns and colored papers. A warm breeze, blowing through the palms, stopped to touch the Christmas trees and make them dance.

"And now it's time for a siesta," said Aunt Valentina, spreading their mats on the floor. "If you're going to stay up until midnight, you'll have to have your siesta."

The children slowly climbed up the ladder and lay down on the floor. That night they would go to church, at the Nativity hour, and after that there would be a midnight feast. Small wonder they couldn't sleep, thinking about it all.

Pedro lay on his back, watching the lizards scamper up the walls in search of mosquitoes. Outside Aunt Valentina was swishing rice back and forth in her flat bamboo basket to let the wind blow the chaff away. She sang happily to herself:

> " 'My nipa house is very small
> But in gathering seeds, it houses them all;
> Sincamas and talong,
> Seguidillas and mani,
> Sitao, batao, patani.' "

Great-aunt Trinidad sat in the doorway, grinding cacao beans with a stone. The smell of chocolate made Pedro hungry. He could smell, too, the chicken *adobo* in the pot on the stove.

Just as he was about to ask for something to eat, he heard the squeaking of cart wheels down the street. He rolled over and looked out the door. There was Domingo, and behind him sat Uncle Manuel and Grandmother Paz with the *tampipi* basket between them.

"Oy!" shouted Pedro, jumping out of the door with one bound. Behind him came Marciana and Juana and Nene. The four of them raced down the street to meet their grandmother.

"Well," said Grandmother Paz, gathering them all in her arms, "if my children can't come 'to kiss the hand of Grandmother' at Christmas, then Grandmother will come to them."

Joyfully they led her back to the house where Aunt Valentina and Great-aunt Trinidad came to the gate to meet her.

"Did you bring my Christmas present?" whispered Pedro, when Uncle Manuel had carried the *tampipi* basket indoors.

"Do you want it now?" asked Grandmother Paz.

"Yes," said Pedro. "I am going to give it to Uncle Manuel."

Grandmother Paz opened the *tampipi* basket and took out a package tied up in red tissue paper.

"Uncle Manuel," called Pedro, "here is a Christmas present for you."

Everyone crowded around to watch Uncle Manuel open the

package from Manila. Out of the red tissue paper came a round black record. "For your victrola," said Pedro.

"For my victrola!" exclaimed Uncle Manuel, beaming. "Where is my victrola?"

The three little girls dragged it from the corner and lifted the lid. They all listened in delight while the music came from somewhere in the box:

> "Jingle bells, jingle bells, jingle all the way,
> Oh, what fun it is to ride in a one-horse open sleigh!"

They loved it. None of them had ever seen snow or even heard of a sleigh, but it was such a jolly tune that they all began to sing with the victrola. The three little girls and Pedro danced round and round the room, until their mother said they'd fall through the floor if they didn't watch out.

"When are we going to give Grandmother Paz her surprise?" asked Nene, in a whisper so loud that it could be heard all through the house. Everyone laughed, while Grandmother Paz pretended she hadn't heard.

Pedro, who was almost bursting with the secret, jumped up. "Right now," he cried, taking Grandmother Paz's hand and leading her down the ladder.

The whole family went with them. Even Great-aunt Trinidad left her sunny doorway and stomped along with her cane. Grandmother Paz was quite breathless by the time she reached the riverbank. "Wherever are we going, Pedro?" she asked, as she followed them through the bamboo grove.

"Here it is!" cried Pedro, who had run on ahead.

Then she saw the wee nipa house sitting in the middle of a tidy yard. In every window hung a star lantern with a long swishing tail.

"It's for you," said Pedro.

"Oh-h-h," breathed Grandmother Paz. "What a dear little house." Then she turned to her grandson. "What did you say, Pedro?"

"It's for you," said Pedro.

Everyone began talking at once, telling Grandmother Paz how Pedro had found the little house and the whole village had helped mend it for her.

Grandmother Paz couldn't say a word. But her shining eyes told everyone she was too happy to speak.

"There is a mango tree near the door," said Nene, remembering that her grandmother liked mangoes.

"So there is," said Grandmother Paz.

"And look!" cried Pedro. "Here is the chicken coop; there are two chickens in it."

"It is just as I have dreamed a little house should be," said Grandmother Paz.

They went inside and lighted the candles in the star lanterns that hung in the windows. Then the neighbors began to come to welcome Grandmother Paz home. Each one brought a gift—a few eggs, or a basket of rice, or even a live chicken to put in her chicken coop.

Uncle Manuel played his guitar. What with the laughing, and the talking, and the singing, and the noise of firecrackers, it was a very gay housewarming.

Darkness came quickly, and outside the Christmas stars twinkled through the palm trees. The candles in the windows lighted the laughing faces of friends and neighbors. Pedro stood in the doorway watching them. He said, "Grandmother, do you think this little old house was ever so happy before?"

"Oh, Pedro," Grandmother Paz laughed, "are you still asking funny questions?"

"You're all right, Pedro," said Great-aunt Trinidad, playfully tapping him on the head with her knuckles. "If you don't ask questions, you'll never know anything."

RUSSIA

(As Reflected in the United States)

A Carol for Katrusia

ANNIE B. KERR

FROM THE TINY kitchen of the Vincents' apartment delicious odors floated out into the narrow court and were wafted away over the snowy roofs of the tenement houses.

Mrs. Vincent sank down on Peter's cot in the dining room and went over in her mind the various items of the Christmas preparations. Her name wasn't Vincent at all, but the children, especially Catherine, had persuaded her several years ago that the name Vincent was much more sensible and practical than their real name, "Vinnichenko." She had, however, stubbornly refused to part with her first name, Katrusia, in spite of the children's objections.

From Peter's cot where she was resting, Katrusia could see a little patch of gray sky through a lacy veil of falling snow. She loved the snow; it reminded her of the far-off steppes of Russia, of bells and sleighs and herself tucked inside a beautifully woven wool *kilim*, speeding through the frosty night. It reminded her of her Cossack father, stamping the snow from his heavy boots before he entered the house, and of her Cossack lover, riding across the plain from the next village where he lived. Her eyes turned from the window and the falling snow to the picture on the wall of a bride and groom in Ukrainian peasant attire. Twenty-five years ago that picture had been taken in Kiev when Katrusia was just seventeen and Vanka twenty. Where was he now, that strong young Cossack, lost these twenty years? Every day she had asked herself that question. Every day during all the weary time in America she had watched for the boat to bring him back to the little family he had sent out from war-torn Russia. Every day she had watched for the letter that never came. Christmas time always brought him to her mind with renewed vividness, for five gay and happy Christmases had they spent together, walking through the snow-drifts at midnight to kneel side by side in the village church and pray at the manger crib of the Christ-child. Indeed, it had been at a Christmas Eve celebration that she had first seen Vanka, the tallest and handsomest of all the village boys, singing the *Kolyadny* from house to house. His eyes had smiled boldly into hers and he had bent low over her outstretched hand which held a coin, as he sang:

" 'Yuletide wakes, Yuletide breaks,
Woman, give me eggs and cakes.' "

The two girls burst noisily into the room, interrupting their mother's reveries. They dropped their clumsy bundles on the floor and drew the gloves from their cold fingers. "*There*, Mamusia." Olga leaned down and rubbed her glowing cheek against her mother's pale one. "We've searched the whole neighborhood for this straw and wheat. It's grand outdoors, just like your old Russia."

Catherine stooped to untie the bundle. "A nice mess we'll have in the house," she pouted.

Katrusia sighed and got up from the cot, the remembrance of days long ago still in her eyes. She and Catherine had had a long and bitter conflict over this Christmas celebration.

"We're American—why should we celebrate Christmas on January seventh, and spend days beforehand cooking more food than anybody can eat?" Catherine had protested.

"Because we're Ukrainians first—before we are Americans—and because we have church on January sixth and seventh and not on December twenty-fourth and twenty-fifth, even here in America," Katrusia had replied. But Catherine was not to be persuaded. She was spoiled, was Catherine, the baby of the family. Russia and Russian ways meant nothing to her. At her age Katrusia was already married, with Catherine in her arms and Peter and Olga clinging to her skirts.

It was really Peter who had saved the day. Peter, who was

always looking out for someone less fortunate than himself; Peter, who when just a little boy had assumed the responsibility of the family.

"Just one more time we shall have a Ukrainian Christmas," Peter had decreed. "I've found two homesick fellows over at Levitsky's rooming house, and I've promised a Christmas Eve celebration that will make them think they're back home in Kiev."

Catherine had turned from him with a little contemptuous sniff. He caught her by the shoulder and shook her gently.

"Don't be so high-hat, young lady. Who knows, perhaps one of them might make a good husband!"

"Yes—a greenhorn from the old country—a *nice* husband!" she had flung back at him.

But anyway, the question of this year's Christmas had been settled, and Katrusia took a week off from the shop in order to clean the apartment and wash all the clothing and bedding. They didn't really need her at the shop, for work was slack. Olga couldn't help her—they were taking inventory in her place—and Catherine always had some excuse for not soiling her pretty hands. But all of them stayed at home on January sixth, working hard to have everything in readiness by the time the first star should appear in the sky.

It was still early when the girls came in with the bundles of hay and wheat, and broke in on Katrusia's reverie. She watched them arrange the wheat in a corner of the dining room, tuck some of the straw under the edge of the tablecloth, and throw the rest on the floor under the table.

"There!" exclaimed Catherine. "For the last time we throw all this litter about."

Katrusia smiled at her rebellious young daughter. "Perhaps—sometime—you understand," she said, fastening her best embroidered apron around her waist. She patted lovingly the broad border of black and red cross-stitch, and wondered if making buttonholes in the tailor shop had spoiled her hands and her eyes for embroidering as she used to do. She left the girls to put the finishing touches to the table and went into the kitchen to be sure the fish in the oven was not getting too brown.

She gave the borsht a swift stirring, set the pan of savory cabbage leaves stuffed with rice on the back of the stove, and wished aloud that Peter would come soon with his two guests, for the dinner was ready, and she was very hungry. The long days of fasting that preceded Christmas had been hard to observe this year; she must be growing old, she thought wistfully. Yet she could still dance the *Hopak* and whirl and stamp as her daughters had never been able to do, and when she stood in her usual place in the very center of the Ukrainian chorus, arrayed in her beautiful costume, with the wreath of gay flowers and ribbons encircling her head, she knew she looked as young and pretty as any of the younger group.

Dusk had begun to gather in the streets, where already the snow had been trampled into mud and slush, when Peter came noisily into the room with his two guests.

Introductions over, they sat down at once at the loaded table, and Katrusia took the first spoonful from the traditional dish of wheat, from which each one must take a liberal mouthful before the remainder of the meal could be eaten.

"By the way, Mamusia," Peter swallowed the hot food hastily, "there are three old fellows over at the boarding house who are coming in to sing for us. They used to sing in the old country on Christmas Eve. They can't find work, and one of them has been in prison for years and lost all his folks. They don't know English and haven't been here long. I hope they'll find the house. I wrote it all out for them to show somebody on the street—'*Vincent*, 185 First Street.' "

Katrusia rose suddenly to hide the tears that welled up into her eyes. How like Peter to invite the poor old men! But he couldn't guess what it would mean to his mother to have them sing. Perhaps it would be, "Yuletide wakes, Yuletide breaks."

"It's just what we need to make the evening perfect, Peter," she said. "I'll save enough of everything, so they can have plenty to eat for once."

Throughout the rest of the meal Katrusia sat on at the head of the table, eating mechanically the food that she had so eagerly prepared. She heard as in a dream the gay talk and laughter of the young people. She stopped them when they threatened to throw to the ceiling a handful of *kutya*—the pudding made of wheat, honey, and poppy seed, which in the old country would bring good luck to all of them could they but make it stick to the roof. She was conscious of Catherine's kindling eyes as one of the young men talked, and was reminded once more of that Christmas so long ago when she had first seen Vanka. She realized dimly that the talk turned to more sober subjects and that scornful Catherine was duly impressed when their guests spoke enthusiastically of the Ukrainian poet Shevchenko, and admired his picture hanging on the wall. But all the time she was back in a little village in Russia, and a young Cossack on a wild horse was riding toward her across the snowy plain.

Then she heard the tramp of feet coming up the stairs, and her eyes glowed as she rose from her chair when Peter threw open the door.

But she sank back with a little sigh. Just three ragged old men, who must be listened to politely, fed, and sent away. They came close to the table and began to sing:

" 'Yuletide wakes, Yuletide breaks,
Woman, give me eggs and cakes.' "

Once more Katrusia rose to her feet, her hand pressed hard against her beating heart. The man nearest her, the one who was most ragged and forlorn, stepped closer to her and the song died in his throat.

"Vanka!" she cried.

"Katrusia?" It was a question and a sob.

Then all was confusion and excitement, explanations, and tears.

It was Peter who fed the two other old men and sent them away; it was Catherine who asked Peter's young friends to go with them to church. Katrusia sat on in the quiet room with Vanka's hand in hers and thanked God for bringing him home on Christmas Eve.

Outside, the roofs and windowsills were white with snow, and church bells were ringing for Midnight Mass.

SWEDEN

The Holy Night

SELMA LAGERLÖF

IT WAS a Christmas Day, and all the folks had driven to church except Grandmother and me. I believe we were all alone in the house. We had not been permitted to go along, because one of us was too old, and the other was too young. And we were sad, both of us, because we had not been taken to early Mass to hear the singing and to see the Christmas candles.

But as we sat there in our loneliness, Grandmother began to tell a story.

"There was a man," said she, "who went out in the dark night to borrow live coals to kindle a fire. He went from hut to hut and knocked. 'Dear friends, help me!' said he. 'My wife has just given birth to a child, and I must make a fire to warm her and the little one.'

"But it was way in the night, and all the people were asleep. No one replied.

"The man walked and walked. At last he saw the gleam of a fire a long way off. Then he went in that direction, and saw that the fire was burning in the open. A lot of sheep were sleeping around the fire, and an old shepherd sat and watched over the flock.

"When the man who wanted to borrow fire came up to the sheep, he saw that three big dogs lay asleep at the shepherd's feet. All three awoke when the man approached and opened their great jaws, as though they wanted to bark, but not a sound was heard. The man noticed that the hair on their backs stood up, and that their sharp, white teeth glistened in the firelight.

They dashed toward him. He felt that one of them bit at his leg, and one at his hand, and that one clung to his throat. But their jaws and teeth wouldn't obey them, and the man didn't suffer the least harm.

"Now the man wished to go farther, to get what he needed. But the sheep lay back to back and so close to one another that he couldn't pass them. Then the man stepped upon their backs and walked over them and up to the fire. And not one of the animals awoke or moved."

Thus far, Grandmother had been allowed to narrate without interruption. But at this point I couldn't help breaking in. "Why didn't they do it, Grandma?" I asked.

"That you shall hear in a moment," said Grandmother—and went on with her story.

"When the man had almost reached the fire, the shepherd looked up. He was a surly old man, who was unfriendly and harsh toward human beings. And when he saw the strange man coming, he seized the long spiked staff which he always held in his hand when he tended his flock, and threw it at him. The staff came right toward the man, but before it reached him, it turned off to one side and whizzed past him, far out in the meadow."

When Grandmother had got this far, I interrupted her again. "Grandma, why wouldn't the stick hurt the man?" Grandmother did not bother about answering me but continued her story.

"Now the man came up to the shepherd and said to him: 'Good man, help me, and lend me a little fire! My wife has just given birth to a child, and I must make a fire to warm her and the little one.'

"The shepherd would rather have said no, but when he pondered that the dogs couldn't hurt the man, and the sheep had not run from him, and that the staff had not wished to strike him, he was a little afraid and dared not deny the man that which he asked.

" 'Take as much as you need!' he said to the man.

"But then the fire was nearly burnt out. There were no logs

or branches left, only a big heap of live coals; and the stranger had neither spade nor shovel wherein he could carry the red-hot coals.

"When the shepherd saw this, he said again, 'Take as much as you need!' And he was glad that the man wouldn't be able to take away any coals.

"But the man stooped and picked coals from the ashes with his bare hands and laid them in his mantle. And he didn't burn his hands when he touched them, nor did the coals scorch his mantle, but he carried them away as if they had been nuts or apples."

But here the storyteller was interrupted for the third time. "Grandma, why wouldn't the coals burn the man?"

"That you shall hear," said Grandmother, and went on.

"And when the shepherd, who was such a cruel and hard-hearted man, saw all this, he began to wonder to himself, 'What kind of a night is this, when the dogs do not bite, the sheep are not scared, the staff does not kill, nor the fire scorch?' He called the stranger back and said to him: 'What kind of a night is this? And how does it happen that all things show you compassion?'

"Then said the man, 'I cannot tell you if you yourself do not see it.' And he wished to go his way, that he might soon make a fire and warm his wife and child.

"But the shepherd did not wish to lose sight of the man before he had found out what all this might portend. He got up and followed the man till they came to the place where he lived.

"Then the shepherd saw that the man didn't have so much as a hut to dwell in, but that his wife and babe were lying in a mountain grotto, where there was nothing except the cold and naked stone walls.

"But the shepherd thought that perhaps the poor innocent child might freeze to death there in the grotto; and although he was a hard man, he was touched and thought he would like to help it. And he loosened his knapsack from his shoulder, took from it a soft white sheepskin, gave it to the strange man, and said that he should let the child sleep on it.

"But just as soon as he showed that he, too, could be merciful, his eyes were opened, and he saw what he had not been able to see before, and heard what he could not have heard before.

"He saw that all around him stood a ring of little silver-winged angels, and each held a stringed instrument, and all sang in loud tones that tonight the Savior was born who should redeem the world from its sins.

"Then he understood how all things were so happy this night that they didn't want to do anything wrong.

"And it was not only around the shepherd that there were angels, but he saw them everywhere. They sat inside the grotto, they sat outside on the mountain, and they flew under the heavens. They came marching in great companies, and as they passed, they paused, and cast a glance at the child.

"There were such jubilation and such gladness and songs and play! And all this he saw in the dark night, whereas before, he could not have made out anything. He was so happy because his eyes had been opened that he fell upon his knees and thanked God."

Here Grandmother sighed and said: "What that shepherd saw we might also see, for the angels fly down from heaven every Christmas Eve, if we could only see them."

Then Grandmother laid her hand on my head and said: "You must remember this, for it is true, as true as that I see you and you see me. It is not revealed by the light of lamps or candles, and it does not depend upon sun and moon, but that which is needful is that we have such eyes as can see God's glory."

Jenny Lind's Yuletide

BURNETTE THOMPSON

JENNY LIND is a legend to all but the oldest living Americans—a symbol to those in middle life, a vaguely familiar name to the younger generation. The Swedish soprano had none of the modern sensational methods of advertising so many employ for self-exploitation; yet the excitement this charming and benevolent girl created in the song-loving world has scarcely been paralleled. Not only in her native country, but in all the capitals of Europe, her name became a household word. Palace doors were thrown open to her; kings, queens, and princesses paid her homage. Then came the famous P. T. Barnum enterprise of bringing the "Swedish Nightingale" to America for a series of sensational concerts covering a period of nearly two years. The furore and ovations that attended her everywhere, from the moment the ship docked in New York, were quite without precedent, though the songstress herself remained at heart and in manner the simple, humble, and childlike character who had once sung to her playful kitten back in Stockholm.

Her character was molded in the true Scandinavian turn—taciturn, earnest, meditative, persevering, faithful, and withal modest and retiring. Her exemplary Christian deeds and personal attributes all but eclipsed the fame of her unusual attainments as an artist. Yet this was the Jenny Lind who wrote from Boston to her home in Sweden: "It was indeed a great joy, and a gift from God, to be allowed to earn so much money and, afterward, to help one's fellowmen with it. This is the highest joy I wish for in this life; everything else has disappeared from the many-colored course of my path on earth. Few know, though, what a beautiful and quiet inner life I am living. Few suspect how unutterably little the world and its splendor have been able to turn my mind giddy. Herrings and potatoes, a clean wooden chair, and a wooden spoon to eat milk soup with—that would make me skip like a child for joy."

Between these lines lay that same nostalgic longing for home which constantly permeated her letters on every departure from Sweden and all that lay nearest her heart, in obedience to the call of art. Her nature was so thoroughly Scandinavian, and her attachment to her own nationality so deep and passionate, that no matter how splendid the opportunity, she was often a victim of a terrible homesickness—an aching void which seemed almost to verge upon physical malady. "One's heart is in one's own country," she once wrote, "and mine, certainly, is Swedish to the very backbone of my body and soul." Yet this highly talented mistress of her art, which she repeatedly claimed as only lent to her by God, knew all too well that it rarely falls to the lot of genius to choose its own sphere of action.

Though Sweden remained ever the veritable home to which Jenny Lind's heart turned with affection, it was in Germany that she found a harbor for her artistic spirit, and in England that she eventually established her own home, reared her family, and had her final resting place. At no time of the year was her longing for the familiar scenes more poignant than at Christmas, not only the time for celebration and feasting, but also one of goodwill and giving pleasure to others. All through life Jenny loved, like a child, her Christmas tree, the home feast, the carefully chosen presents. Those who knew her can recall no time when she could more deliciously abandon herself to brimming joy than at a children's Christmas party. All the old Swedish merriment and motion would bubble up, and her face would laugh all over with exuberant humor.

It is small wonder, then, that the Christmas of 1841 loomed dismal and cheerless to the young girl—the trying year she spent in Paris as a student of the great singing teacher, Signor Garcia. Not only had the extreme fashions, manners, and language been very foreign to her, but there had been those terrible weeks of uncertainty as to whether she would ever sing again at all, and then the long, tedious process of rebuilding, step by step, the strained, tired voice. In spite of outward poise, the future seemed very uncertain and she felt, without doubt, that a debut as a European artist was impossible in gay, worldly, sophisticated Paris.

When Christmas time drew near, she thought of all the festivities and preparations which were a part of the Swedish Christmas celebration—the scrubbing, cleaning, and baking that were going on in every home. On St. Lucy's Day her mother would be baking *lussekattor*, the round, swastikalike saffron buns with raisins. And then there were the lighted trees and the candles in the windows on Christmas Eve, for no family was ever too poor not to provide some kind of decoration. But one kind friend was thoughtful enough to send Jenny a box of Swedish rye bread which is baked in large, thin sheets with a hole in the middle so it can be hung up on a string. To Madame

Lindblad, the wife of the Swedish composer, she wrote, "Do you know what I am doing, besides writing to you? I am munching away—at what?—just guess—at a bit of genuine Swedish *Knackebröd* which Herr Blum has brought. Ah! think of me, when you go to the *Julotta*, for it is the most glorious thing your poor Jenny knows of." But the French lady with whom she boarded had sensed the girl's loneliness and had thoughtfully arranged for another talented singing student to come and help brighten the evening. To Madame Lindblad, again, she later wrote: "Christmas Eve passed off better than I expected; for Mademoiselle du Puget went to fetch the dear sweet *Nissen*, and all of a sudden, as I was standing in my room alone, she came creeping in to me. We sang duets together—but my thoughts strayed homeward."

Little did the discouraged but persevering young lady know then that in the space of only three years she would be the idol of the operatic stage, both in her beloved city of Stockholm and on all of the Continent. Yet each triumph only seemed to make her more conscious of her imperfections and ever distrustful of her own artistic powers. She set exacting standards for herself, and her performances often fell short of her own ideal, even though passing the approval of stern critics.

During the course of the years 1844–1847, which were spent mostly in Germany, with occasional appearances in Sweden, Finland, and Denmark, she became the admired friend of many a social circle, including not only royalty but musicians and men of letters. In Sweden her intimate friends were A. F. Lindblad, Geijer, and Josephson, composers whose vocal lyrics were inspired by her voice. On the Continent, Meyerbeer, Mendelssohn, Spontini, Rossini, Moscheles, Chopin, Robert and Clara Schumann, and Brahms gave her unreserved devotion. Most notable of all these friendships was that with Mendelssohn. They were first introduced to each other in 1844 at the Wichmann home in Berlin. Jenny Lind had come to look upon this place almost as if it were her own home, though in a sense she had never known a real one. She loved Frau Wichmann like a sister and enjoyed the genuine hospitality she extended. The deep regard for each other's talent and character was instantly mutual between Jenny Lind and Mendelssohn. That his subsequent letters, advice, encouragement, and stimulating personality had a tremendous influence on her is unquestioned. And that she directly inspired much of his oratorio *Elijah* is authoritatively stated, the most famous soprano passages having been written with the memory of her voice in mind. To friends he wrote: "Tell her that no day passes that I do not rejoice that we are both living at the same epoch and have learned to know each other and are friends, and that her voice sounds so joyous, and that she is so exactly what she is."

Similarly, it was at the home of friends in Copenhagen, Denmark, in 1843, that Jenny Lind first met Hans Christian Andersen, poet and dean of fairy-tale writers. That the tall, loosely jointed figure with the homely, childlike face became hopelessly infatuated with the singer has been no secret in biographical history, and excerpts from his own diary testify to his unrequited love. He began to send her daily offerings such as poems, bouquets, and small presents. Yes, he felt, here was someone who could understand him and his ugliness, someone who like himself had risen from a poor home, not gifted with any beauty, but transfigured by a kind of spiritual light. Very shortly he made known his feelings in a four-line verse she found tucked in her luggage:

"TO JENNY LIND

You sang—I listened, enchanted singer,
And yet my best song you will receive.
One forgets the artist for the woman—
I do not sing, my heart beats too strong."

When she returned to Copenhagen three years later to sing at the Royal Theater, in the midst of cheering crowds the pathetic Hans Christian was waiting patiently on the wharf, holding some "Welcome" verses. The artist in her naturally responded to the artist in him, and she was truly fond of him—but as a kindred sister only. During this short stay, Andersen was often her companion, as she felt sorry for his loneliness. But though she treated him with kindness and affection, he became acutely aware of his position, and an entry in his diary after a particularly enjoyable afternoon reveals: "Jenny is very sweet to me. I am glad and hopeful—although I know!" All further wooing on his part was definitely ended when, during a farewell dinner, she drank a toast to him—as a "brother." He knew these were no idle words. But while the sister was wholly a sister, it was sometimes difficult for the brother to feel he was that and nothing more. Yet he found in her an inspiring friendship which was renewed and confirmed again and again in those places where these two enjoyed almost identical popularity.

Perhaps it was chance, but far more likely deliberately planned, that Hans Christian Andersen found himself in Berlin at the same time as Jenny Lind—the last days of December, 1845. She had come on from Leipzig for a limited engagement at the Berlin Opera House. Andersen's trip through Germany thus far had resembled a royal progress. Poets, philosophers, and princes flocked around him, publishers fought over him, and painters insisted on doing his portrait. Yes, in Berlin he was a society lion—a sort of masculine "Jenny Lind," as he jokingly referred to himself. Yet amid this revelry and festivity there remained one evening that found him sitting alone in his hotel room, quite sad and downcast. And that was Christmas Eve. Andersen himself tells of this in his autobiography after describing how he had been feted by Berlin society: "Amid all this superfluity of kindness and interest in making my stay there agreeable, one evening stood empty, unoccupied—one evening in which I suddenly felt loneliness in its most crushing form. That was Christmas Eve, just that one evening that with the mind of a child I saw in all its festive glory, when it seemed that I must see the Christmas tree, rejoice in the joy of the children, and see their elders become children once more. On just this evening when, as I heard later from the many who would have been glad to extend their hospitality, everyone believed that I had already accepted an invitation to some place where I preferred to be, I was all alone in my room at the hotel, thinking of my home in Copenhagen. Jenny Lind was in Berlin, was giving concerts there; the public admired and worshiped her not only as an artist but also as a woman, and this double worship created such enthusiasm that the theater was literally stormed when she sang. In every town, in all places to which I came, the talk was of her, but for me this talk was not needed, for she was deep in my thoughts, and it had been my fondest dream to spend Christmas Eve with her. I was convinced that, should I at that time be in Berlin, this holiday evening would be spent in her society. It was such a firm conviction with me that I refused all invitations from my friends in Berlin, and then when the evening came—I had not been invited by Jenny Lind, and I sat all alone in my hotel, feeling so forsaken. I opened my window and looked up at the starry heavens; that was my Christmas tree. I felt so bruised in spirit. Others may call me sentimental; they know the word—I know the feeling.

"The next morning I was vexed, childishly vexed at my wasted Christmas Eve, and I told Jenny Lind how cheerlessly I had spent it. 'I thought you were in the company of princes and princesses,' she said. Then I told her that I had refused all invitations in order to be with her, and that I had looked forward to this for a long, long time, that it was for this very reason that I had come to Berlin during the Christmas holiday. 'Child,' she said, smiling, stroked my brow with her hand, laughed at me, and continued: 'It never occurred to me, and besides I was invited out, but now we must have Christmas Eve all over again, and I shall have the tree lighted for the child. New Year's Eve we shall have the tree at my home.' "

And so on the very last evening of the year, Sylvester Eve, three children of the North, Andersen, Jenny Lind, and her companion, had Christmas all over again in their own way, and Andersen was the child for whom the little, garlanded tree was lighted. It was also decked with pretty presents, all for the honored guest. With girlish delight, Jenny presented each one to Andersen and asked him to guess the contents. She rocked with delight when he almost mistook a cake of expensive soap for a choice cheese! And from his voluminous pockets, Andersen brought forth his gifts for the ladies—bonbons, toiletries, and various trinkets. The party was complete in every way, for there were tea, ices, and an elegant supper. How wonderfully kind she could be, the poet thought with a sigh. And how she smiled and rejoiced with sisterly feeling when he told her of his recent honors. She showed such genuine enthusiasm over the ring he had just received from the Grand Duke of Oldenburg, and the blue velvet album from the Prussian Crown Princess. And, of course, she had immediately noticed the splendid decoration he wore conspicuously on his coat—the Red Eagle of the Third Class, bestowed by the King of Prussia! His innocent-like pride over his treasures was so appealing that Jenny looked at him almost pityingly and lightly murmured: "Andersen, you're a child. Such a child you are!" Then, going to the piano, she took from the music rack an album of songs in manuscript which had just arrived by post from Leipzig. It was a Christmas gift from Felix Mendelssohn. On the cover he had drawn some decorations in pencil and watercolor. Being an amateur drawer himself, Andersen was delightfully amused by the efforts of the composer. Jenny also read aloud some of the portions of the letter accompanying the gift, the translation of which is as follows:

Leipzig, 23d December, 1845

My dear Fräulein,

For your dear, kind, friendly letter I would so much like to thank you, and say how much pleasure you have given me with the letter and its kind thought of me. You know, of course, what pleasure you give me by remembering me, and yet, gratitude is never expressed in words—just when one would like to be fluent, one never succeeds. Your letter reminds me of Lindblad; he also had never mastered German grammar, and yet wrote better and more fervently than most Germans can. I have remembered some of the passages in his letters all my life, and I can say the same of yours. You remember what the Queen of Prussia said to you, "*Verändern Sie sich nur nicht*" ("only don't change"). I think I should have invented that remark if she had not said it first, and as often as I have read your letters, and as often as I think of you, I always come back to those words.

Tomorrow is Christmas Eve, and ever since you left Leipzig, I have wished for permission to be among those who bring you gifts. There will be many to do so, but none heartier or more sincere than I, and so I beg you to accept these songs. I now feel that I want to say something about increasing the number of song composers who crowd round you—but I have taught myself to refrain, as I think you would find it *mal-place!* But above all I must apologize for the drawings, but the fault lies with the compliments I received at the Court Concert—when you said that you, too, could dance, I determined to do some drawings for you as well (badly) as I could. This time, however, many interruptions have made them less good than I hoped; please forgive—at least I have not omitted the *rosen och de bladen* (Swedish) and the gold stars, and the Swedish bread.

I would again specially thank you for the Swedish bread. Please, dear Fräulein, send us sometime such a loaf, and don't forget it as long as you are in Berlin; we all enjoy it so much, and eat it up with so much pleasure; and the children jump for joy when a loaf comes from Fräulein Lind, and I thank you for sending one yesterday. The other day the children saw your portrait on the street, and they ran to it and said it was you, and when I asked them if they had read your name, they said, no, they recognized you, but the portrait was not like you. I wanted to make an instructive remark, that it must have been like you for them to have recognized it, but I left it alone.

And when we got home, there was your bread, and in the evening, there was your letter. That was a very happy day, my dear Fräulein, and I shall not forget it. And now I must close my letter, as the post is going which will bring it to you tomorrow. If I were in Sweden, I should throw the packet in at your door (should I not?). If I were in Berlin, I should take it to you—and that is what I would soonest do. As it is, the postman will take it, and I beg of you to think of me tomorrow evening.

As far as I am concerned, you know that at every happy festival and on every serious day I think of you, and you have a share in them, whether you like it or not. But you wish it, I am sure, and you know from me that it is the same with me and never will be otherwise.

Always your friend,
Felix Mendelssohn-Bartholdy

And I wish you a Happy Christmas!

It was natural that these two honest-hearted souls should both contribute some of their respective talents to the festive occasion, so as they sat together on the sofa, Andersen read aloud to her the fairy tale she had always said she loved best—"The Ugly Duckling." Perhaps both saw snatches of their own lives reclothed in the charming story. Then the prima donna, who only the night before had scored one of her greatest triumphs on the operatic stage, went to the little piano and sang some of the simple songs Andersen loved best. A warm, contented feeling of peace and a gentle, Christmas happiness flowed through his long, gaunt frame as he sat listening with dreamy, half-closed eyes, wondering how life could be so beautifully kind. The two friends were to meet again very soon, they discovered, as Jenny was scheduled to sing in Weimar about the same time that Andersen expected to arrive there. For that reason he eagerly expressed the hope that he might be able to arrange some introductions for her and also accompany her on a tour of the many interesting sights to be found there. It so happened that on the way Andersen stopped off a few days at Dresden to visit his close friend, the Crown Prince of Saxony, and his diary describes this charming incident: "An evening that for me was particularly interesting I spent with the royal family, who received me most graciously. Here reigned the same quiet that is found in private life in a happy family. A whole troupe of amiable children, all belonging to Prince John, were present. The youngest of the princesses, a little girl who knew that I had written the story of 'The Fir Tree,' began familiarly her conversation with me in these words: 'Last Christmas we also had a fir tree, and it stood in this very room.' Afterwards, when she was taken to bed earlier than the others, and had wished her parents and the king and queen 'good night,' she turned round once more at the half-closed door and nodded to me in a friendly manner, and as though we were old acquaintances. I was her prince of the fairy tale."

Though Andersen basked contentedly in the brilliant splendor of fame and thoroughly enjoyed the itinerant life, the Swedish soprano grew more and more weary of the ceaseless traveling, social demands, and increasing professional complexities that naturally attended such a career. The woman in her was fully as strong as the artist, and her longing for a quiet home and normal, simple living was asserting itself more and more emphatically, as shown in her letters. She saw the contented family life of the Mendelssohns, the Schumanns, and many others, and her lonely heart dictated that she would gladly exchange all her triumphs for a small measure of such happiness. But circumstances thus far had not granted her this desire. She resigned herself to what she believed was God's will in this respect and dedicated her talents more than ever to charitable acts. And there were many contracts yet to be fulfilled, particularly the long-standing one in England. It was during this period that Jenny Lind decided to retire from the stage and confine herself to concert and oratorio performances alone. The decision may have been the composite result of many influences, dominated by her own pious devotion to certain religious principles. She had witnessed the estrangement it had made between her and her betrothed, Herr Julius Gunther, a tenor with the opera company in Stockholm. Then, too, her love for singing oratorios had increased, no doubt a Mendelssohn influence. Also, a new admirer, Captain Harris of the British Army in India, to whom she became engaged, had demanded that she give up the stage because of the family's religious views toward it. In fact, they went as far as to think the stage was the invention of the devil and that his sweetheart would have to atone by a life of repentance for ever having appeared on it. They wanted her solemn promise actually written in the marriage settlement! However, the captain had not the slightest hesitancy in coming into possession of the money that had been earned there, and sternly informed her that it would be "unscriptural" if she were to control her own fortune after marriage. Fortunately, the affair ended as it should have, even though a lasting love, a happy marriage, and a home seemed more remote than ever.

About this time the initial overtures were being made by Barnum to bring the famed singer to America. In spite of her recent resolves, she was overjoyed at the prospect of a long concert tour, for it seemed an answer to her desire for ample funds toward charitable enterprises, particularly the endowment of schools and hospitals in Sweden. To a friend she confided: "And so I go there in this confidence; and I pray God in heaven, out of a full heart, that he will guide me thither, as ever before, with his gentle hand; and will graciously forgive me my sins and my infirmities. I shall have much to encounter; it is a very big undertaking. But since I have no less of an aim before me than to help in widening God's Kingdom, the littleness of life vanishes in face of this!"

This was the Jenny Lind, now thirty years of age, that Phineas Barnum, the great American showman, brought to America in the fall of 1850 to enter upon a series of 150 sensationally successful concerts in all the leading cities. Her earnings were prodigious for that day. But she was noted less for what she earned than for what she gave away. The entire receipts from the tour were reserved for charity.

Perhaps credit can be given to Jenny Lind for decorating one of the earliest Christmas trees in this country—at least in the South, for it was at Charleston that the singer, her assisting artists, and manager happened to be during the holiday season. Secretly, Jenny secured a tall, stately tree and decorated it elaborately in the drawing room of her apartments. Then she invited the entire company for Christmas Eve, not disclosing the surprise, of course, that she had in store. When the group arrived, she met them in the outer salon, and after graciously extending her greetings, she invited them to step into the next room, for there they would see something wonderful! What a surprise and joy it was to all when they saw the lighted tree so beautifully decorated and laden with small gifts for everyone. It was especially touching to the hearts of those countrymen who had a memory of such a Christmas tree in their own homes far across the water. And the well-known Swedish verse in a picture book came to the minds of several.

> "*Ljusen tändas,*
> *barnen bländas,*
> *allting ändas*
> *under fröjd.*"

Then came the opening of the packages, accompanied with much laughter and innocent joking. For weeks Jenny had been selecting each gift with much care and thought. Such wild guessing they made on the contents! Now, the esteemed orchestra conductor naturally expected some appropriate musical gift, such as a baton or a tuning fork. Imagine the merriment of the party when, after removing the fortieth wrapper, he held up some Cavendish tobacco! Meanwhile, Barnum was busily engaged in removing the countless wrappings on his present. It turned out to be a marble statue of Bacchus, the god of wine and revelry. Knowing of his extremely temperate habits, everyone thoroughly enjoyed the prank. After this joyous part of the occasion, the hostess herself read a Christmas meditation and sang a few songs. Then all partook of a delicious supper which included even *julgröten*—the rice pudding always served at a Swedish Christmas Eve feast.

The next year Jenny Lind was quietly married to Otto Goldschmidt, her accompanist, in Boston. He had been sent for when her first accompanist became very ill and could not continue on the tour. The two had met previously in England, but little suspected the event that would come to pass. Goldschmidt was nine years her junior, and a Jew by birth. But he was baptized into the Christian faith, and Jenny Lind herself stood as his sponsor. From the wedding day on, Jenny insisted on being addressed and billed as Mme. Lind-Goldschmidt. From all indications, this marriage proved to be an ideally happy one, and Jenny in later years confessed in a letter to a friend that "it has been all that I could ever have wanted."

After several short concert trips in Europe, the Goldschmidts established their home in England, and Jenny began that life of semiretirement and domesticity for which she had long yearned. Her active participation in musical affairs did not cease entirely. There were the usual charity concerts, many oratorio performances, and she liked to assist her husband in his musical projects, particularly the Bach Choral Society. But she was primarily interested in her home and children, of whom there were three, two sons and a daughter. The latter, who was endowed with musical talent, has written a book and several reminiscences concerning her mother.

We learn that their home was an open house for the intelligentsia of the time, with many an evening devoted to music and lively talk, often climaxed with Jenny's singing favorite songs and her husband's accompanying her in his own perfect way. She took a personal interest in the daily household tasks, instructing the cooks in the preparation of Swedish dishes, and doing fine handwork and sewing. "Indeed," Mrs. Raymond Maude writes, "to the end of her days she retained all the simplicity of habits and thoughts of her early Northern life. Her religious beliefs were very strong, her faith simple and innocent, and her Bible-reading was taken very seriously. . . . This mother of mine was the most lovely granny, and never could do enough to show her affection. She even wrote to my babies in magnificent, large handwriting, with affectionate superscriptions on the envelopes, much to the edification of the Surrey postman, no doubt. Her Christmases were real Christmases as far back as I can remember, and the six weeks preceding were periods of mystery and expectancy. It was not only an expenditure of money, but each present to relative, friend, or servant was carefully thought out, tied up, and labeled with some appropriate phrase or joke, and the carol singing, which preceded the lighting of the tree, she always led and accompanied, in a delightful way, on her dear little old harmonium."

The beloved singer's later years were filled with much suffering from ill health, and she died in 1887 at her home in Malvern Hills, in her sixty-seventh year. Her funeral was attended by many representatives of royalty as well as of the arts, and a last tribute was paid to her memory when the Dean of Westminster Abbey acceded to a widely signed petition for a memorial to her—an honor heretofore accorded no uncrowned woman. The plaque was placed in Poets' Corner beneath that of Handel, of whose *Messiah* she was so great an interpreter.

Many of her programs opened with the beautiful aria "I Know that My Redeemer Liveth." It was always noted that she placed a certain accent on the word "know," thus making the utterance, as it were, a personal confession of faith. Some years after Jenny Lind's death, Signor Garcia, who was then ninety years of age, wrote a letter to Mr. Goldschmidt, citing the fullness, the purity, and the perfection of her singing in the oratorio *The Messiah.*

And so, when one glances at the bronze relief of the womanly face in Westminster Abbey, above which is inscribed the text she loved to express, the tomb of Handel nearby seems a fitting companion. The world remembers Jenny Lind, not alone as an artist, but as a woman of noble character and as a philanthropist. In proportion to her personal endowments, she answered the Christian challenge that is made in some capacity to every living soul—that the world ought to be somewhat happier and better for one's having come into it.

SWITZERLAND

Christmas in the Alps

BERTHA T. HARPER

IT WAS a white Christmas in the Swiss Alps. The mountains looked like big, frosted cakes, and the dark fir trees of the forest were wrapped in a mantle of white. In every direction there were masses of glistening snow. The only sound in this still world came once a day from the shrill whistle of the four o'clock train which passed through there.

On one of the mountain slopes, beside the railroad track, there stood a little hut. In the summertime there was a flower garden around it, and its bright red geraniums gave friendly greeting to the passengers on the daily train. But now all the little flowers were sleeping under the blankets of snow.

In this little hut lived the railroad guard with his wife and their five-year-old son, Jimmie. It was the duty of Jimmie's father to make a daily trip, halfway to the next guard house, to see if everything along the track was safe. Then, when the train passed by, he stood in front of the guard house waving a blue and white flag. This was a signal to the engineer that the track was clear, and that he could pass on.

Now it happened that on the day before Christmas the guardsman became quite ill. He thought that by lying down a little while he would soon be all right. His wife had brought in a little fir tree from the forest behind their house just to make it seem like Christmas. She had nothing to trim it with except a few strips of red and blue paper that she had saved from last year. They were very poor, and because they lived so far from the village, few people ever came to visit them.

Instead of getting better, Jimmie's father soon became worse.

His wife felt that she must hasten to the village and get the doctor, if he would be willing to come all that distance through the snow. She felt that she must get help somehow, and the only way was to tramp several miles over the woody hills and through the heavy snow as best she could.

The man was soon in a sound sleep and breathing heavily. It was nearly three o'clock, and by four the train would be due, when he must by all means be at his post of duty.

The mother took little Jimmie to the big clock on the wall, and showed him where the largest hand should point at ten minutes to four. She made Jimmie promise that he would rouse his father at that time, so that he could stand by the track with the flag when the train passed by.

"Now, Jimmie, be sure to wake your father when you see the clock hand reach this place," she said. "See, I will paste this little bit of red paper at the right point so you won't miss it when the big hand gets there. Watch the clock, little man, and don't fail to waken your father! For if he does not stand there when the train comes along, he will lose his job, and we will have no other place to go."

Then she went to the cupboard and emptied the little broken pitcher where she kept her money, hoping to find enough to buy Jimmie the little toy engine for which he had been wishing so long. But, alas! there were just a few copper coins and one small silver piece, barely enough to pay for the medicine she would have to get.

With a sigh she wrapped a shawl around her, and put on her husband's tall boots to make ready for the long tramp through the snow.

"I will be home before dark," she said, as she kissed Jimmie good-by. "Now, be sure to watch the clock and waken your father on time!"

"I'll be a good boy and do as you told me, Mother," Jimmie called after her, waving his little hand from the doorstep.

Then he went in and got his much worn picture book. Seating himself right in front of the clock, he kept looking at it every now and then.

Tick-tock, tick-tock, tick-tock, on went the clock. There was no other sound in the little room except the heavy breathing of the sleeper.

Slowly, slowly, the big hand crept steadily on, while Jimmie kept watching it. Nearer and nearer it came to the red mark. He hardly waited until it had reached the point before he began tugging at his father.

"Wake up, Daddy!" he called. "The train will soon be here!" But there was no sign of the sick man's awakening. The little boy screamed loudly in his ear, and shook him with all his might, but the man could not be roused. The clock hand had almost passed the mark by now.

Suddenly Jimmie knew that he must take his father's place. He quickly slipped on the big coat his father wore, and, snatching the little signal flag, posted himself outside the door.

He was none too soon. Already he heard the train whistle around the curve, and the little hut shook as it came thundering along. Jimmie's heart went pit-a-pat, but he held tightly to the flag, waving it as the signal to the engineer.

The train slowed up. When the engineer and fireman saw the queer little figure in a man's coat which dipped down into the snow, and gravely holding the flag in his little hands, they stopped the train long enough to learn what the trouble was.

The passengers, looking out of the car windows, smiled and waved at the little rosy-cheeked boy standing there.

Among the people on the train was a young American lady. "Isn't he a dear?" she said to her companion. "He looks as if he had just stepped out of a storybook."

Then she took a little purse out of her bag, and hastily wrote something on a slip of paper. She tossed them to the little guardsman, saying a few words in English which, of course, this Swiss child could not understand.

Jimmie went back into the hut with a very glad feeling, because he had been able to take his father's place. Then he looked into the little purse. How surprised he was to find it full of shiny, silver coins, and among them the slip of paper with words written upon it that he could not read.

Now he would have something to decorate the little Christmas tree with, and how surprised his mother would be!

While the father slept on, Jimmie placed all the silver pieces, one by one, upon the green branches of the tree. There seemed to be no end of them. How the little tree sparkled with the strange ornaments! He pinned the slip of paper to the top branch, then clapped his hands with glee.

Just as it was growing dark and one could hardly see anything in the room but the shining bits of silver, there was a tinkling of sleigh bells outside the door. Jimmie hurried to the window and saw his mother and the village doctor climb down from the sleigh. The good man had come right along as soon as he heard of the father's illness.

The doctor had not only brought Jimmie's mother back with him, but he had a big basket filled with red apples, gilded nuts, and spicy cookies, which his wife had sent to the little boy in the mountains. Best of all, there was a large package of toys which the doctor's own little boy had wanted to share with lonely Jimmie. There was a red engine, too, which would run around all by itself when wound up!

What joy there was in the little hut all at once! The doctor examined the sick man and said: "We will have him out of this very soon. The long sleep has done him a world of good." Then, wishing them a happy Christmas, he rode away in his sleigh.

When she saw all the silver pieces scattered over the tree, Jimmie's mother thought it must be a dream! She could not believe her eyes!

Then Jimmie told her of the beautiful lady at the car window who had tossed the purse to him, and said words he could not understand. How proud his mother was when she learned that her little boy had taken his father's place so bravely!

"Why, here is the lady's name!" she said, as she noticed the little white paper pinned at the top of the Christmas tree. "It reads, 'Miss Merry Christmas'!"

"That is a queer way of spelling 'Mary,' though," said the mother. "She must be a foreigner. But blessed be her name, whoever she is. Now if only we knew her address, we could write and thank her for the happiest Christmas that ever came to this house."

But I am afraid the letter would never have reached her.

THE UNITED STATES
(ALASKA)

An Indian's Christmas Gift

MARGARET W. EGGLESTON

LIQUOR AND LAZINESS had combined to make Big Moon one of the most unmanageable Indians in all the countryside. He was a rough, strong bully. He feared no one, respected no law. Women and children ran if they saw him coming. Men stayed at home on guard when he had one of his drunken bouts. Often, at night, he would creep up near to a village and bellow like a mad bull, then laugh, uproariously, when he knew that he had awakened and frightened the families who lived there.

One day, as Big Moon was hurrying through the woods during a severe storm, a tree struck by lightning fell directly in his path, pinning him to the ground. He was badly hurt, and lay suffering excruciating pain with no one to comfort him. At last he heard footsteps, so he called for help. When he saw that the traveler was a small man, and also that he was a missionary whom Big Moon had taken special pains to annoy, the Indian was angry and began to curse loudly. How could a little man free him from the tree? What would the missionary do when he found that he had his enemy in his power? Big Moon wondered.

The missionary hurried to the injured man, tried to lift the tree, spoke kindly to Big Moon, and then hurried away, leaving the Indian thinking he did not care to help. Soon, however, he came running back, accompanied by his wife and grown son. All were carrying tools or ropes. While the two men cut limbs from the tree, the woman carried water from a spring and gave the sick man a drink, bathing his aching head, and assuring him that he would soon be free again. It seemed an endless time before the two men had cut enough foliage away so that they could lift the trunk. Then, with great effort, the three propped it up, and helped the man from beneath it.

Now the missionary was also a doctor, so he examined Big Moon very carefully. Several bones were broken, and he had many bad bruises. Knowing that the man must be removed as quickly as possible, he sent the boy back home to get a mattress from one of the beds. On this they drew the wounded man to their home. His bones were set and his cuts were cleansed. For weeks he was graciously cared for by the missionary's wife. As he watched the Christians in their home, a new purpose was formed in his mind, and he became very much ashamed of the life he had led. He knew he could never be a strong man again, but he determined that he would help the missionary in his work, in appreciation of the love and care that had been shown him.

Big Moon went to work, and soon the schoolhouse, which had been used as a church, was not large enough. He persuaded the Indians to help in building a new, suitable church. When a Sunday school was started, Big Moon rounded up the children, bringing some to the school on his pony. He became a strong, eager Christian, and his influence was felt for miles around.

After several years, the wife of the missionary became ill, and they moved back to Pennsylvania. Big Moon had no wife and no home, so he felt sad and lonely. At last, he decided to follow them, working his way as he went. It was hard work, for often an Indian was not trusted, could not find employment. When his clothes began to wear out, he settled down in a factory town for the winter, so that he could earn more.

One night a man had promised to meet him on a certain corner to tell him of work that was to be done by Big Moon. He waited one hour, then two. His missionary friend had taught him that a Christian kept his word. Big Moon had said that he would be there, so he waited, moving back and forth, incessantly, because of the cold.

Suddenly a man ran out of an alley, knocking the Indian down in his haste to get away. Quick as lightning, Big Moon was up and after him, intending to thrash the man for knocking him down. Two more men ran from the alley and grabbed Big Moon as he gained on his man. They knocked him down, kicked him, clubbed him, and then ran, thinking Big Moon was dead. But he wasn't. After a time, he crawled to his room, to stay there for two days without help or food, though his body was tortured with his wounds.

On the third day a policeman came and arrested Big Moon. There had been a robbery three days before, and three men had gone to the police station to tell of an Indian who had run from the alley, tried to kill them, but had gotten away. They brought his shoe; they described his face. The policeman found the mate to that shoe under Big Moon's bed; his cuts and bruises corroborated what the men had said, so Big Moon was sentenced to five years in jail. What chance had a friendless Indian, a tramp, against such evidence?

Now, Big Moon had told a straightforward story, and he resented his sentence. In the courtroom he had recognized one of the men as the person who had first run from the alley; hence, he was probably the thief. Big Moon clenched his fists when the man testified against him, and said, "I get you; I get you yet." He was hurried off to jail. His clothing, containing the address of his friend, the missionary, was burned, and Big Moon was alone and desolate.

Months went by, and Big Moon grew accustomed to the dark, dirty cell. Every evening he repeated the texts which he had learned at that little Sunday school which he had helped to build. He fought hard to get the bitterness out of his life, for he really wanted to be Christian. He knew that if he did not get it out before he left the jail, he would surely kill one, at least, of the men who had sent him there.

It was the day before Christmas, and all the prisoners were sent to the chapel to hear a well-known quartet sing Christmas carols. Big Moon chanced to be in the front row. As the quartet rose to sing, he recognized his enemy, and his enemy recognized Big Moon; his face grew pale and tense. Big Moon's eyes never left his face. An hour later the man came to the Indian's cell.

"Big Moon," he said, "I have often thought of you. I hoped you were out by this time. Here is a little gift to help cheer your Christmas. I hope when you do get out, you will cease being a tramp and go to work." A Christmas card was pushed through the bars, containing a dollar bill.

All the old bad temper rose in Big Moon. If he could have reached the man, he would have choked him. How dared he come and offer Christmas money when he was the real thief? All night the tempest raged within him, but little by little the memories of that fallen tree, of the missionary and his family, and of the little white church on the hilltop began to help Big Moon. He must forgive as he had been forgiven.

Christmas morning he asked the guard if he might have a Christmas card; then he asked the guard to write a message for him on the card. It was:

"I give you no money for Christmas. I give your money away. I give, instead, my forgiveness. It is better to stay here than to be outside big walls with guilty mind. Big Moon."

The card was taken to the office, addressed to "The Tall Man Who Sang the Christmas Songs." The guard told the jailer of the money which he had taken for Big Moon to a man who had a sick child and needed money. The jailer read the card; then he passed it to a famous attorney who was sitting in the office.

"That man is innocent," said the attorney. "I'll look into that, I think." He talked with Big Moon, and then traced his life story to see if it was true. He found the missionary, and brought him to Illinois to testify for Big Moon. He checked on the bank accounts of the singer and his friends. Then Big Moon was freed, and the singer took his place in the cell.

"I send good card. I make good friend. I learn it is good to be Christian," said Big Moon, as he started with his friend for his new home in the East. "I try harder next time to forgive soon."

(BOHEMIAN-AMERICAN)

A Bohemian Christmas in Chicago

CLARA INGRAM JUDSON

AS DAYS GREW shorter and Christmas neared, the Kovec cottage was full of secrets and fragrant odors. The minute Anna and Rosie got home from school, they put on big aprons and helped with baking. Two great stone jars, bought to replace the pair that had to be left in Prague, were already half full of spicy goodies. This day the mother was making the decorated *dorts*.

"Papa and Jan will like these pastries," Rosie remarked gleefully as she washed her hands and tied on her apron. She was careful to say nothing about her own sweet tooth—if she was very helpful, perhaps her mamma would let her eat one when the pastries came from the oven. She fetched the rolling board and pin, got the jar of raisins, and began seeding them without being told.

"These are going to be the best I've ever made," Mrs. Kovec predicted. "I'll make a big, big batch too. Anna will be here with the marketing soon. Your papa and Jan went up to the city and will be late. We have plenty of time. Quince is cooked—with cinnamon and ginger as your papa likes it. If you think you can do it nicely, maybe I'll let you put pastry strips on top of a few apple *dorts* and we'll have those for supper."

"Oh, I can, Mamma! I'll make them the prettiest we ever had!" Rosie watched her mother's skillful fingers mix and mold the dough.

"Now then," her mother said, as she picked up the rolling pin, "tell me the Christmas poem. Tell it in English, Rosie, every word."

When Anna arrived with the marketing, Rosie was reciting English words:

" ' 'Twas the night before Christmas and all through the house,
Not a creature was stirring, not even a mouse.' "

Anna set the basket down and recited with Rosie:

" 'The stockings were hung by the chimney with care,
In hopes that Saint Nicholas soon would be there.' "

"My teacher says Saint Nicholas doesn't ever come on his day—not in America," Anna remarked. "That's why you were disappointed, Rosie." Poor Rosie! She had hung up her stocking, as always, on December sixth—Saint Nicholas' Day, which Bohemian children call "Saint Mikulas' Day"—but next morning there it hung, limp and empty. Papa had been indifferent to her disappointment.

"Didn't I tell you that in America, December sixth is nothing? Nothing but another day! Didn't I tell you that in America, Saint Nick comes on Christmas Eve?"

"Not till then?" Rosie had been anxious and disappointed for days. She had not quite believed this postponement.

Now she whirled on Anna, her outstretched hands sticky with raisins.

"You think he will come Christmas Eve, don't you, Anna?" she asked eagerly.

"I'm certain of it!" Anna said. Why shouldn't she be certain? She had been knitting mittens diligently after Rosie went to sleep, mittens with a snowflake pattern across the back, just what Rosie would like. Jan was carving a wooden doll and painting on it an excellent face that smiled mischievously, and Mamma had made a whole new outfit for the doll, American clothes, very stylish. But of course Rosie knew nothing of this, though she did notice that her family took sudden interest in getting her to bed. Unfortunately, she was never able to keep awake and see what they were up to.

"I'm as sure Saint Nick is coming as—as—I am that we're making pastries. You hang up your stocking Christmas Eve!" By now Anna had her apron on and was at work too.

When Jan and his father returned about eight o'clock, the house was full of the smell of sugar and spice and browning fruit juices. They sniffed hungrily. It was a good thing Anna had the supper ready, and that the decorated tarts were put out of sight. Otherwise, many might have been eaten up then and there.

Later, when hunger was satisfied, Kovec sat back in his chair and remarked, "How would you like a treat tomorrow evening?"

"Tomorrow!" Anna said. "Tomorrow is Saturday." She had looked forward to Saturday all week, for that was the time when she worked at the music shop.

"Tomorrow," Kovec said, and he was not thinking of a music shop. He winked at Jan like a conspirator, and they grinned at each other. "How would you like to go to the city?"

"Already we are in Chicago," Anna said, wondering what he was planning.

"Yes, Chicago," Kovec agreed. "But now I mean State Street —the fine stores, the bright lights."

"And get Jan's face cut by those gangs?" Mrs. Kovec retorted.

Jan waved that aside. "No danger now, Mamma. A Bohemian is on the City Council."

"Frank Dvorak is an American," Kovec corrected Jan. "If he wasn't an American, he couldn't be elected to the council."

"Yes," Jan agreed. "But he is Bohemian-born. The first to be elected to a city office. You told me yourself, Papa. He is trying to make people understand us. He says that is the way to stop fights. Miss Jane Addams helps him. There's no danger now, Mamma."

Mrs. Kovec began to stack the dishes and clear a place for newspapers.

"Well, maybe," she granted.

"Where are these bright lights, Papa?" Rosie asked.

"In the store windows. On the streets. Oh, there are so many— you shall see tomorrow, Rosicka."

Next morning Anna hurried to the shop, planning to get lots of practicing done. A good thing she was early, too, for Mr. Pakos was out, and a customer arrived five minutes after Anna.

He was a plump, blond young man, older than Karel and eager for his purchase.

"I want a ————," he shouted so loudly in English that Anna could not understand him.

"I know some English," she said, speaking very slowly and precisely. "Again tell me, please."

The man came closer and shouted louder, as people often do when trying to make another understand.

"I want a ————," and then Anna was lost again. The word he yelled was one she had not heard. She shook her head, and he grinned at her.

"Show me," she suggested, meaning for him to point out in the case the thing he wanted to buy.

Instead he began to laugh. "Dumb Boho!" he chuckled, but as he said them, the words had no sting. He set his hat at an angle, tossed back his head, and marched around the room in a pompous way. Anna could hardly keep her face straight.

"You parade?" she exclaimed, but he frowned. No, "parade" was not the word. He marched again, now shouting, "Dum-dicky-dick! Dum-dicky-dick! Now!"

"Oh," Anna giggled at his playacting. "You mean *buben!*"

"No," he exclaimed. "And this is not a joke!"

"No joke," Anna agreed, though she could hardly keep from laughing. "*Buben?*"

"No *buben!* Listen, Boho!" He marched again, sticking out his stomach and pounding with his fists. "Dum-dicky-dick—catch on?"

Anna ran to the big cupboard in the corner, flung open the door, and pulled out a drum, the only drum Mr. Pakos had in the shop.

"There—*buben!*" she cried.

He grabbed for it, grinning, "Drum, yes. I said drum," he shouted, laughing. "You're not so dumb as you pretend." He flung down five dollars, picked up the drum, and left, chuckling.

A few minutes later Mr. Pakos came back and Anna reported what had happened.

Pakos laughed. "That Johnson! Yes, it is all right, Anna.

He borrows my drum sometimes—comes from north of the Park to get it. Leaves me five dollars, and I give back four when he brings the thing back." He started for the back room with his bundles. "No wonder you could not understand him." He laughed till the tears ran down his thin face. "That Swede! His English is no better than yours."

Anna was still gay when she finished the work and began to practice. That was a good way to start a day. She wished more customers would come.

As soon as she got home, the Kovecs set out for the city. Rosie held her father's hand and skipped briskly to keep up with him. "I can say some new words, Papa," she boasted.

"Do I know them?" he asked, half teasing her.

"You never said them, Papa—not that I've heard."

"Then tell me!"

" 'Merry Christmas!' Guess what that means!"

"Well, what?"

"*Vesele Vanoce!*" Rosie answered. "It is the same, my teacher says. So this year I shall wake you up and tell you 'Merry Christmas,' and now you'll know what it means, Papa."

"*Vesele Vanoce!* Merry Christmas!" Mrs. Kovec repeated. "Only the sound of the words is different."

"The verses too," Papa said. "Tell them now while we walk." So Rosie said twelve Christmas verses on the way to the stores.

"Since the elevated is getting built," Kovec told them soon, "this part of the city is called 'The Loop' because the tracks go around and around." He swung his arms about, but the others paid little heed to his information, for at that minute they turned into State Street.

The wonder of that sight made their eyes open. Horses drawing handsome carriages clattered over cobblestone streets. Great drays, some pulled by double mule teams, some by enormous horses, were piled high with packing cases. Window displays glittered. Getting across the street was an exciting adventure, with everyone in fine spirits. The policeman at the corner helped Mrs. Kovec to the curb and grinned at Rosie. In all the crowds, no one seemed cross or hateful—people hurried by, smiling, laden with parcels, laughing because Christmas was near. The fragrance of pine and blazing candles scented the air and added to the holiday feeling.

Anna was too thrilled for talk. State Street was a beautiful sight—buildings, higher than any in Prague, were so tall that roofs were lost in the sky. No wonder Papa calls them "sky-scrapers"! she thought. Windows glowed brightly. Each tall building was like a great box, punctured with tiny holes and stood on end, with a candle burning inside. Anna had made such a box many a time, but never had she thought to see a likeness so vast in size.

"Come this way—through the crowd, if you want to look in the windows," Papa said.

Anna wanted to linger at each window, but her father dragged them on.

"You have something special to show us, Papa?" Anna guessed when he had pulled her away from a window display of musical instruments.

"That's right!" he admitted. "Now come—in the next block!" He took her arm, and Rosie's on his other side. Jan was looking after his mother.

"There, look!" He stopped in front of a great window. The girls stared in wonder. Jan, who had seen it before but had kept it a secret, was as pleased as they were.

On the floor of the store window was the model of a small city. At least, it seemed to be a city, Anna thought. She saw buildings, many, many buildings, some large, some small, all gleaming white. Walks were threadlike lines between tiny gardens. Boats of various sorts—tiny steamers, gondolas, canoes, barges—floated on mirror lakes. Tiny flags of many sorts fluttered from turreted roofs. Little people, men, women, and children dressed smartly in fashion, strolled on the walks, crossed on bridges, descended wide, white steps.

"Is it fairyland?" Rosie whispered, awed by the lovely sight.

"That is a model of the World's Fair," her father told her. He said the words proudly, as though he had had a part in the wonder himself.

" 'World's Fair?' " Anna repeated his words.

"Some call it the Columbian Exposition, some the White

City," Kovec told her. "World's Fair is good enough for me." He spoke all these words in English. Indeed, the more her father worked with men in the city, the more he spoke English and the easier his words came.

"Shall we see it, Papa?" Anna asked.

"Oh, yes!" Kovec spoke with sureness. "And look, down here—see this long street—there?" He pointed to one side of the modeled scene. "That is the Midway, the place for pleasure, some call it. Down there, near the end, is where Jiri is having his Bohemian glassworks. That will be important for us, so look well."

"Where the Bohemian glass exhibit will be, Papa?" Anna asked. For months before they left Prague she had heard talk of the fine Bohemian glass that was to be sent to the American Fair.

"Some glass will be on display in this building." Kovec pointed to a rectangular white building, the largest on the grounds and topped with flags of many nations. "But in there, it will be shown under the Austrian flag— Austrian glass indeed!" His voice was bitter. "Jiri wants to show that Bohemians make the most beautiful glass in the world. That's why he's bringing over his skilled workers. He'll let people see how the glass is made and see the Bohemians who produce it." Kovec had a keen interest in this project, his family knew; even talking of it thrilled him.

"The apartment building Papa will help build is near here." Jan pointed to the west end of the Midway. "I'll be working with him—right there." They pressed close to the glass of the store window. For the first time "World's Fair" meant something real—more than mere words or a dream.

"And if it turns out that there's a Bohemian Day at the Fair, the exercises will be here—in Festival Hall. And the gymnastic exhibit will be here." He pointed to an open court between the buildings.

"Did I tell you that Mr. Pakos says Dvorak will come to play?" Anna wondered.

Jan grinned at her. She had told everything about that evening with Mr. Pakos a dozen times over.

"Rosie! You were to select a new star for our Christmas tree—remember, Papa? We'd better hurry or the stores will close." Jan dragged her away from the enchanting window.

From that evening the days raced by until Christmas. Friday Jan had no work, and he was glad of that, for he was needed at home. He bought a little Christmas tree on Blue Island Avenue and fixed a firm base for it in a corner of the front room. He fixed a great stack of wood for his mother. Cousins from the northwest side, the Kafkas, whom they had not seen since arriving, were having Christmas Eve dinner at the Kovecs'. With the Dubecs, that would make a big party to entertain.

Anna unpacked the manger scene, brought from Prague, and set it up under the tree. Mamma cooked a big supper for Friday, because Saturday, the twenty-fourth, the family would fast until the evening star came out. Rosie thought this was a terrible ordeal and began complaining even as she was setting Friday's supper table.

"Think of all we'll be doing." Anna tried to divert her. "We'll take down the big bed. We'll put up a long table in the front room. Mamma will set the bread and make the *bousky*."

This was a favorite sweet bread with chopped, candied fruits inside. "She has started the roe soup and stuffed the goose, already."

"Wouldn't there be a little crumb of something I could eat?" Rosie teased.

"Not a morsel!" her mother said, vexed at the teasing. "What's come over you, Rosie?"

"Maybe tomorrow you will really see the Golden Pig," Jan encouraged Rosie. "Remember Grandma always said that if you didn't eat a crumb all day, you'd surely see the Pig—and that means luck for a whole year?"

"I would rather have food than luck," Rosie replied. "Anyway, I'm lucky enough."

"You're in luck now," Jan laughed, "because you're going to help me tie candles on this tree. Wait, I'll climb on a chair and you pass them to me."

Finally Christmas Eve arrived. Errands were done; the table

looked sumptuous—almost every inch was covered with good food. The tree with the manger scene below was perfect.

"Don't muss the curtains, Rosie," Mrs. Kovec said nervously. She looked around to see that everything was right.

"I'm looking for the evening star, Mamma!" Rosie cried. "I see it! I see it! Look!" She let the starched lace curtains drop and ran to the table. "Now may I have a *dort?*"

"Wait till Anna brings the light, Rosicka," her mother said. "When I was a little girl, we didn't hurry to end the fasting. We watched the ceiling patiently after we saw the evening star, knowing that if we glimpsed the shadow of the Golden Pig up there, we'd have luck and plenty for a year."

Anna lighted the lamp in the kitchen and slowly walked into the front room. Rosie peered at the ceiling, watching dusky shadows flit across as Anna moved.

"I see it! I see it, Anna," the little girl shouted, dancing up and down and clapping her hands. "He's there—no! Anna, you moved! Now he's gone! But I did see the Golden Pig this time, I did, Mamma."

Anna set the lamp on the shelf. Mrs. Kovec studied the table for anything forgotten, Papa came hurrying in, and the guests were at the door. The Christmas celebration had begun.

(BOSTON)

Christmas Waits in Boston

EDWARD EVERETT HALE

I

I ALWAYS GIVE myself a Christmas present. And on this particular year the present was a carol party—which is about as good fun, all things consenting kindly, as a man can have.

Many things must consent, as will appear. First of all, there must be good sleighing, and second, a fine night for Christmas Eve. Ours are not the carolings of your poor, shivering little East Angles or South Mercians, where they have to plod around afoot in countries where they do not know what a sleigh ride is.

I had asked Harry to have sixteen of the best voices in the chapel school to be trained to eight or ten good carols without knowing why. We did not care to disappoint them if a February thaw setting in on the twenty-fourth of December should break up the spree before it began. Then I had told Howland that he must reserve for me a span of good horses and a sleigh that I could pack sixteen small children into, tight-stowed. Howland is always good about such things, knew what the sleigh was for, having done the same in other years, and doubled the span of horses of his own accord, because the children would like it better, and "it would be no difference to him." Sunday night, as the weather nymphs ordered, the wind hauled round to the northwest and everything froze hard. Monday night things moderated, and the snow began to fall steadily, so steadily— and so, Tuesday night the Metropolitan people gave up their unequal contest, all good men and angels rejoicing at their discomfiture, and only a few of the people in the very lowest "Bolgie" being ill-natured enough to grieve. And thus it was that by Thursday evening there was one hard, compact roadway from Copp's Hiss to the Boneburner's Gehenna, fit for good men and angels to ride over, without jar, without noise, and without fatigue to horse or man. So it was that when I came down with Lycidas to the chapel at seven o'clock, I found Harry had gathered there his eight pretty girls and his eight jolly boys, and had them practicing for the last time:

" 'Carol, carol, Christians,
Carol joyfully;
Carol for the coming
Of Christ's Nativity.' "

I think the children had got an inkling of what was coming, or perhaps Harry had hinted it to their mothers. Certainly they were warmly dressed, and when, fifteen minutes afterward,

Howland came round himself with the sleigh, he had put in as many rugs and bearskins as if he thought the children were to be taken newborn from their respective cradles. Great was the rejoicing as the bells of the horses rang beneath the chapel windows, and Harry did not get his last "*da capo*" for his last carol, not much matter indeed, for they were perfect enough in it before midnight.

Lycidas and I tumbled in on the back seat, each with a child on our lap to keep us warm; I was flanked by Sam Perry, and he by John Rich, both of the mercurial age, and therefore good to do errands. Harry was in front somewhere, flanked in likewise, and the twelve other children lay in miscellaneously between, like sardines when you have first opened the box. I had invited Lycidas because, besides being my best friend, he is the best fellow in the world and so deserves the best Christmas Eve can give him. Under the full moon, on the snow still white, with sixteen children at the happiest, and with the blessed memories of the best the world has ever had, there can be nothing better than two or three such hours.

"First, driver, out on Commonwealth Avenue. That will tone down the horses. Stop on the left after you have passed Fairfield Street." So we dashed up to the front of Haliburton's palace, where he was keeping his first Christmastide. And the children, whom Harry had hushed down for a square or two, broke forth with good, full voice under his strong lead in

" 'Shepherd of tender sheep,' "

singing with all that unconscious pathos with which children do sing, and starting the tears in your eyes in the midst of your gladness. The instant the horses' bells stopped, their voices began. In an instant more we saw Haliburton and Anna run to the window and pull up the shades, and, in a minute more, faces at all the windows. And so the children sang through Clement's old hymn. Little did Clement think of bells and snow, as he taught it in his Sunday school there in Alexandria. But perhaps today, as they pin up the laurels and the palm in the chapel at Alexandria, they are humming the words, not thinking of

Clement more than he thought of us. As the children closed with

> " 'Swell the triumphant song
> To Christ, our King,' "

Haliburton came running out, and begged me to bring them in. But I told him no, as soon as I could hush their shouts of "Merry Christmas"; we had a long journey before us, and must not alight by the way. And the children broke out with

> " 'Hail to the night,
> Hail to the day,' "

rather a favorite—quicker and more to the childish taste, perhaps, than the other—and with another "Merry Christmas" we were off again.

Off, the length of Commonwealth Avenue, to where it crosses the Brookline branch of the Mill-Dam, dashing along with the gayest of sleighing parties as we came back into town, up Chestnut Street, through Louisburg Square, we ran the sleigh into a bank on the slope of Pinckney Street in front of Walter's house, and before they suspected there that anyone had come, the children were singing,

> " 'Carol, carol, Christians,
> Carol joyfully.' "

Kisses flung from the window; kisses flung back from the street. "Merry Christmas" again and a "goodwill," and then one of the girls began:

> " 'When Anna took the baby,
> And pressed his lips to hers' "—

and all of them fell in so cheerily. Oh, dear me! It is a scrap of old Ephrem, the Syrian, if they did but know it! And when, after this, Harry would fain have driven on, how the little witches begged that they might sing just one song more there, because

Mrs. Alexander had been so kind to them when she showed them about the German stitches. And then up the hill and over to the North End, and as far as we could get the horses up into Moon Court, that they might sing to the Italian image man, who gave Lucy the boy and dog in plaster when she was sick in the spring. For the children had, you know, the choice of where they would go; and they select their best friends, and will be more apt to remember the Italian image man than Chrysostom himself, though Chrysostom should have "made a few remarks" to them seventeen times in the chapel. Then the Italian image man heard for the first time in his life:

" 'Now is the time of Christmas come,' "

and

" 'Jesus in his babes abiding.' "

And then we came up Hanover Street and stopped under Mr. Gerry's chapel, where they were dressing the walls with their evergreens, and gave them

" 'Hail to the night,
Hail to the day.' "

And so down State Street and stopped at the Advertiser office, because when the boys gave their Literary Entertainment, Mr. Hale put in their advertisement for nothing, and up in the old attic there the compositors were relieved to hear

" 'No war nor battle sound,' "

and

" 'The waiting world was still.' "

Even the leading editor relaxed from his gravity and the "In General" man from his more serious views, and the *Daily* the next morning wished everybody a "Merry Christmas" with even more unction, and resolved that in coming years it would have a supplement, large enough to contain all the good wishes. So away again to the houses of confectioners who had given the children candy, to Miss Simonds' house, because she had been so good to them in school, to the palaces of millionaires who had prayed for these children with tears, if the children only knew it, to Dr. Frothingham in Summer Street, I remember, where we stopped because the Boston Association of Ministers met there, and out on Dover Street Bridge, that the poor chair mender might hear our carols sung once more before he heard them better sung in another world where nothing needs mending. . . . O, we went to twenty places that night, I suppose; we went to the grandest places in Boston, and we went to the meanest. At nine we brought up at my house, D Street, three doors from the corner, and the children picked out their very best for Polly and my six little girls to hear, and then for the first time we let them jump out and run in. Polly had some hot oysters for them, so that the frolic was crowned with a treat. There was a Christmas cake cut into sixteen pieces, which they took home to dream upon; and then hoods and mufflers on again, and by ten o'clock or a little after, we had all the girls and all the little ones at their homes. . . .

II

Lycidas and I both thought that the welcome of these homes was perhaps the best part of it all, as we went into these modest houses, to leave the children, to say they had been good, and to wish a "Merry Christmas" ourselves to fathers, mothers, and to guardian aunts. . . . Here was brave Mrs. Masury. I had not seen her since her mother died. "Indeed, Mr. Ingham, I got so used to watching then, that I cannot sleep well yet o'nights; I wish you knew some poor creature that wanted me tonight, if it were only in memory of Bethlehem." . . . "What can I send to your children?" said Dalton, who was finishing sword blades. (Ill wind was Fort Sumter, but it blew good to poor Dalton, whom it set up in the world with his sword factory.) "Here's an old-fashioned tape measure for the girl, and a Sheffield wimble for the boy. What, there is no boy? Let one of the girls have it, then; it will count one more present for her." And so he pressed his brown-paper parcel into my hand. From every house, though it were the humblest, a word of love, as sweet, in truth, as if we could have heard the voice of angels singing in the sky.

I bade Harry good night; took Lycidas to his house, and gave his wife my Christmas wishes and good-night; and coming down to the sleigh again, gave way to the feeling which I think you will all understand, that this was not the time to stop, but just the time to begin. For the streets were stiller now, and the moon brighter than ever, and the blessings of these simple people, and of the proud people, and of the very angels in heaven, who are not bound to the misery of using words when they have anything worth saying—all these wishes and blessings were round me, all the purity of the still winter night, and I didn't want to lose it all by going to bed to sleep. So I put the boys all together, where they could chatter, and then, passing through Charles Street . . . I noticed the lights in Woodhull's house, and, seeing they were up, thought I would make Fanny a midnight call. She came to the door herself. I asked if she were waiting for Santa Claus, but I saw in a moment that I must not joke with her. She said she had hoped I was her husband. In a minute was one of those contrasts which make life, life. . . . Poor Fanny's mother had been blocked up in the Springfield train as she was coming on for Christmas. The old lady had been chilled through, and was here in bed now with pneumonia. Both Fanny's children had been ailing when she came, and this morning the doctor had pronounced it scarlet fever. Fanny had not undressed herself since Monday, nor slept, I thought, in the same time. So while we had been singing carols and wishing Merry Christmas, the poor child had been waiting, hoping that her husband or Edward, both of whom were on the tramp, would find for her and bring to her the model nurse, who had not yet arrived, nor had either of the men returned. Professional paragons, dear reader, are shy of scarlet fever. I told the poor child that it was better as it was. I wrote a line for Sam Perry to take to his aunt, Mrs. Masury, in which I simply said: "Dear

Mamma, I have found the poor creature who wants you to-night. Come back in this carriage." I bade him take a hack at Barnard's, where they were all up waiting for the assembly to be done at Papanti's. I sent him over to Albany Street; and really, as I sat there trying to soothe Fanny, it seemed to me less time than it has taken me to dictate this little story about her before Mrs. Masury rang gently, and I left them, having made Fanny promise that she would consecrate the day, which at that moment was born, by trusting God, by going to bed, and going to sleep, knowing that her children were in much better hands than hers. . . .

And so I walked home. Better so, perhaps, after all, than in the lively sleigh with the tinkling bells. What an eternity it seemed since I started with those children singing carols!

> "Within that province far away
> Went plodding home a weary boor;
> A streak of light before him lay,
> Fallen through a half-shut stable door
> Across his path. He passed, for naught
> Told what was going on within:
> How keen the stars, his only thought,
> The air how calm and cold and thin,
> In the solemn midnight,
> Centuries ago!"

"Streak of light"—is there a light in Lycidas' room? They are not in bed? That is making a night of it! Well, there are few hours of the day or night when I have not been in Lycidas' room, so I let myself in by the night key he gave me, and ran up the stairs—it is a horrid, seven-storied, first-class apartment house. For my part, I had as lief live in a steeple. Two flights I ran up, two steps at a time—I was younger then than I am now—pushed open the door which was ajar, and saw such a scene of confusion as I never saw in Mary's overnice parlor before. Queer! I remember the first thing that I saw was wrong was a great ball of white German worsted on the floor. Her basket was upset. A great Christmas tree lay across the rug, quite too high for the room; a large, sharp-pointed Spanish clasp knife was by it, with which they had been lopping it; there were two immense baskets of white-papered presents, both upset; but what frightened me most was the center table. Three or four handkerchiefs on it—towels, napkins, I know not what—all brown and red and almost black with blood! I turned, heartsick, to look into the bedroom, and I really had a sense of relief when I saw somebody. . . . Lycidas, but just now so strong and well, lay pale and exhausted, . . . while over him bent Mary and Morton. I learned afterward that poor Lycidas, while trimming the Christmas tree and talking merrily with Mary and Morton—who, by good luck, had brought round his presents late and were staying to tie on glass balls and apples—had given himself a deep and dangerous wound with the point of the unlucky knife, and had lost a great deal of blood before the hemorrhage could be controlled. Just before I entered, the stick tourniquet which Morton had temporized had slipped in poor Mary's unpracticed hand, at the moment he was about to secure the artery. . . .

"O Fred," said Morton, without looking up, "I am glad you are here."

"And what can I do for you?"

"Some whiskey, first of all."

"There are two bottles," said Mary, "in the cupboard behind his dressing glass."

I took Bridget with me, struck a light in the dressing room (how she blundered about the match), and found the cupboard door locked! Key doubtless in Mary's pocket—probably in pocket of "another dress." I did not ask. Took my own bunch, willed tremendously that my account-book-drawer key should govern the lock, and it did. If it had not, I should have put my fist through the panels. Bottle marked "bay rum"; another bottle with no mark; two bottles of Saratoga water. "Set them all on the floor, Bridget." A tall bottle of cologne. Bottle marked in manuscript. What in the world is it? "Bring that candle, Bridget." "*Eau distillée*, Marron, Montreal." What in the world did Lycidas bring distilled water from Montreal for? And then Morton's clear voice from the other room, "As quick as you can, Fred." "Yes! in one moment. Put all these on the floor, Bridget." Here they are at last. "Corkscrew, Bridget."

"Indade, sir, and where is it?" "Where? I don't know. Run as quick as you can, and bring it. His wife cannot leave him." So Bridget ran, and I meanwhile am driving a silver-pronged fork into the Bourbon corks, and the blade of my own penknife for the other side.

"Now, Fred," from Morton, within. "Yes, in one moment," I replied. Penknife blade breaks off, fork pulls right out, two crumbs of cork with it. Will that girl never come?

I turned round; I found a goblet on the washstand; I took Lycidas' heavy clothes brush and knocked off the neck of the bottle. . . . It smashed like a Prince Rupert's drop in my hand, crumbled into seventy pieces—a nasty smell of whiskey on the floor—and I, holding just the hard bottom of the thing with two large spikes running worthless up into the air. But I seized the goblet, poured into it what was left in the bottom, and carried it in to Morton as quietly as I could. He bade me give Lycidas as much as he could swallow; then showed me how to compress the great artery. When he was satisfied that he could trust me, he began his work again, silently. . . . When all was secure, he glanced at the ghostly white face, with beads of perspiration on the forehead and upper lip, laid his finger on the pulse and said: "We will have a little more whiskey. No, Mary, you are overdone already; let Fred bring it." The truth was that poor Mary was almost as white as Lycidas. She would not faint—that was the only reason she did not—and at the moment I wondered that she did not fall. Bridget, you see, was still nowhere.

So I retired again, to attack that other bottle. Would that Kelt ever come? I passed the bell rope as I went into the dressing room, and rang as hard as I could ring. I took the other bottle and bit steadily with my teeth at the cork, only, of course, to wrench the end of it off. Morton called me, and I stepped back. "No," said he, "bring your whiskey."

Mary had just rolled gently back on the floor. I went again in despair. But I heard Bridget's step this time. She ran in, in triumph, with a screwdriver!

"No!" I whispered. "No. The crooked thing you draw corks with," and I showed her the bottle again. "Find one somewhere and don't come back without it."

"Frederic!" said Morton. I think he never called me so before. . . . "Frederic!" "Yes," I said. But why did I say "Yes"? "Father of Mercy, tell me what to do."

And my mazed eyes, dim with tears—did you ever shed tears from excitement?—fell on an old razor strop of those days of shaving, made by C. Whittaker, Sheffield. The Sheffield stood in black letters out from the rest like a vision. They made corkscrews in Sheffield too. If this Whittaker had only made a corkscrew! And what is a "Sheffield wimble"?

Hand in my pocket—brown-paper parcel.

"Where are you, Frederic?" "Yes," said I for the last time. Twine off! Brown paper off! And I learned that the "Sheffield wimble" was one of those things whose name you never heard before, which people sell you in Thames Tunnel, where a hoof cleaner, a gimlet, a screwdriver, and a corkscrew fold into one handle. "Yes," said I again. "Pop," said the cork. "Bubble, bubble, bubble," said the whiskey. Bottle in one hand, full tumbler in the other, I walked in. Morton poured half a tumblerful down Lycidas' throat that time. . . . I found that there was need of it, from what he said of the pulse when it was all over. . . .

This was the turning point. He was exceedingly weak, and we sat by him through the night, . . . but there was no real danger after that.

As we turned away from the house on Christmas morning—I to preach and he to visit his patients—he said to me, "Did you make that whiskey?"

"No," said I, "but poor Dod Dalton had to furnish the corkscrew."

And I went down to the chapel to preach. The sermon had been lying ready at home on my desk, and Polly had brought it round to me, for there had been no time for me to go from Lycidas' home to D Street and to return. There was the text, all as it was the day before:

"They helped every one his neighbor; and every one said to his brother, Be of good courage. So the carpenter encouraged the goldsmith, and he that smootheth with the hammer him that smote the anvil."

And there were the pat illustrations, as I had finished them yesterday. . . . And I said to them all, "O, if I could tell you, my friends, what every twelve hours of my life tells me—of the way in which woman helps woman, and man helps man, when only the ice is broken, how we are all rich as soon as we find out that we are all brothers, and how we are all in want, unless we can call at any moment for a brother's hand—then I could make you understand something, in the lives you lead every day, of what the New Covenant, the New Commonwealth, the New Kingdom, is to be. . . ."

But when we had our tree in the evening at home, I did tell all this story to Polly and the bairns, and I gave Alice her measuring tape, precious with a spot of Lycidas' blood, and Bertha her Sheffield wimble. "Papa," said old Clara, who is the next child, "all the people gave presents, did not they, as they did in the picture in your study?"

"Yes," said I, "though they did not all know they were giving them."

"Why do they not give such presents every day?" said Clara.

"O child," I said, "it is only for thirty-six hours of the three hundred and sixty-five days that all people remember that they are all brothers and sisters, and those are the hours that we call, therefore, Christmas Eve and Christmas Day."

(KENTUCKY)

Christmas at Thunder Gap

KATHERINE O. WRIGHT

OUTSIDE THE TALL, clear window a star hung in the blue Kentucky evening. It shone into the church house upon Mary, singing to her Babe in the straw—and Stacy Ellen, peeping through the cedar boughs that made the whole place sweet, caught her breath at the scene. There came the shepherds, wearing striped homespun, and there the kings, the Wise Men, bearing gifts. That "Least One" reminded Stacy Ellen of the baby sister she'd be seeing tomorrow when she went home up Thunder Gap. Because of the baby, she had almost run away last autumn, soon after Pappy had left her in the school. It had been hard enough leaving Pappy and Mammy and the five young-uns—but leaving the Least One, whom she had loved and tended from birth, had been almost more than she could bear.

Now she glanced with ecstatic eyes across the swelling music, beyond the light that shone from the manger, to the faces of the other boys and girls uplifted in the half darkness of the church house, and wondered if they were half as happy as she. Was this really Stacy Ellen of Thunder Gap, wearing a flowing robe, a blue ribbon holding the dark hair off her forehead? She pinched one hard little hand beneath its flowing sleeve. Yes! It was Stacy Ellen all right, seeing the Christmas play at the settlement for the first time, and taking part in it too. Heaving a sigh of contentment, she thought, "I'm glad now I tromped on my homesickness for the sake o' larnin'."

Peeping through the cedar boughs, she forgot she had never worn a ribbon before; she almost forgot to sing with the other angels! Then her voice welled up with theirs:

> " 'Glory, in the highest, glory,
> Peace on earth, goodwill toward men!' "

As she sang, longing swept over her to take Christmas home to Thunder Gap. But, lawsy, there wouldn't be much chance for Christmas at home. Mammy was so busy with a houseful of young-uns and Pap had his hands full feeding and clothing them, not to mention helping send her to school.

Later, the whole school trooped out into the starry night to receive gifts from a growing hemlock tree that blossomed with red, gold, and blue lights. What a sight, what a sight! The shadowy mountains rising about the dark valley, and the glory of the lighted tree; all the young-uns shouting and singing and unwrapping presents. Stacy Ellen received a beautiful box of handkerchiefs, a box of pencils, and a whole box of candy. It was marvelous, and she stifled an unruly longing for another tree—a tree that would bear gifts for Mammy, Pappy, the five, and the Least One, up Thunder Gap.

"Good night! Merry Christmas!" the boys and girls shouted when the last package had been unwrapped, for tomorrow they'd be starting home with the rising of the sun.

In her tiny room Stacy Ellen smiled as she drew her blue robe over her dark hair, and carefully folded her ribbon. "With mighty nigh a week to ponder, 'pears like a body as chock full o' Christmas as I am ought to think up something!" she told the starry night.

Next morning, at the crack of dawn, she tied her braid with its usual string, packed her possessions in a bundle, and fastened it, with her best shoes, on the end of a stick. After she had helped with the breakfast dishes—for she worked her way in the school—she donned her old brown coat and red cap and started out, hoisting her bundle stick gunwise over her shoulder. Closing the big gate across the road, she climbed up on its bars a moment to look at the pretty houses of log and green wood scattered over the valley. Her eye followed the chimney smoke, up and up, to the top of the ridge that rose like a wall behind the school. The sun ball was just looking over, and its rays lay up there like a golden veil caught in the bare branches of timber.

"I'll have to come back," she told herself wistfully. "Three months ain't near enough to git larnin'." Then she jumped off the gate bar and ran after the other boys and girls.

There were eight of them going her way, but gradually they parted company, some to go up one creek, some down another. Stacy Ellen felt lucky. She had only eighteen miles to walk and all day to walk it. The tall, long-legged boy who strode beside her had fifty miles to go, and would spend tonight at his uncle's, part way. They all had some such journey to make and thought little of it.

"Ye're the fastest-walkingest boy I ever did see, Zack!" Stacy Ellen announced to the long-legged one, and he slackened his pace and looked down at her.

"However will ye git home so far by your lonesome?" he inquired.

"It's easy," she told him. "All I do is follow this creek to where Yancy Creek flows into it. I follow Yancy to its watershed, and t'other side the ridge I'll find a spring that is the headwaters o' Crazy Creek. Crazy does a sight o' wanderin', but it'll lead me home!" She had a determined look in her blue eyes.

The boy gazed at her with admiration. "Ye'll git thar," he said.

The creek they walked beside shuttled through the mountains so that it was sometimes hard telling which was east, which west. Now the sun shone on the brown water before them, now it glanced from rhododendron leaves behind them, but they trusted that creek, and, with true mountaineer instinct, followed it through the wilderness. At last it was the turn of the long-legged boy to strike out over a high ridge.

"Whoo-ee-ee!" From the summit he called down the "sang cry" to Stacy Ellen.

"Whoo-ee-ee!" She flung back the old cry her grandparents had used when out gathering ginseng, because it carried through the mountains farther than any other.

When the call was a mere echo from the ridge top, Stacy Ellen was alone in the wilderness. She walked along, her bundle bobbing behind her red cap. Now that she was by herself, she could plan some way to share Christmas with the folks at Thunder Gap.

"It's harder than nine times seven, take away five, carry three!" she sighed, wrinkling her brow.

In her bundle she had tucked one of the handkerchiefs for Mammy, and a pencil for Pappy, and there was the candy for the young-uns. But, lawsy! What was one little box of candy? Why, Aaron, her next oldest brother, could eat it in a few mouthfuls. She longed to have a new calico dress for Mammy, and some play toys for the young-uns—and Pap—he'd hankered after a flashlight for a month o' Sundays! Picking her precarious way across foot logs and rolling rocks that might have thrown her into the creek, she pondered about Christmas.

Presently she heard a roar ahead of her and knew that Yancy

was pouring its waters into the creek beside her. Hurrah! That was where she turned off to cross the ridge. The sun ball was straight overhead when she bent her back and started up the steep slope. As she climbed, her bundle stick cut first into one shoulder, and then into the other, as she shifted it, and her face grew warm and red as her cap. After two hours she reached the watershed and looked down the other side of the mountain. Somewhere in the tangle of valleys far below was home—Thunder Gap. A lump came into her dry throat.

Dropping down beside the tiny spring that was the head-waters of Crazy Creek, she ate her lunch, still pondering her problem. Of course, she could make a wreath for the fireboard, a lovely wreath such as she had learned to make at school; and then there might be sorghum-molasses taffy—happen Mammy could spare the 'lasses. She had not got far with her plans when she noticed that the sun was sliding down the sky. Jumping up, she followed the silver trickle from the spring, down and down, its voice growing louder until it became Crazy Creek, a wild torrent in a hemlock gorge. Darkness lurked beside it, and by the time Stacy Ellen's foot touched the bottomland, she cast a shadow in moonlight. She was tired, but she felt safe now, for she knew every step of the way. It was all so peaceful in the bottomland; hayricks seemed resting for the night, and she liked to hear the satisfied cluck of the chickens as they roosted in the trees. Far ahead, up the Gap, she saw a light, and knew that Mammy had left the door open to welcome her.

"That you, leetle gal?" a voice called. It was Pappy, come to meet her.

Mammy made a silhouette against the firelight in the door-way, the Least One in the crook of her arm. The five young-uns hugged Stacy Ellen and took on, but Mammy was the say-nothing kind. Only from the look of her eyes could Stacy Ellen tell how glad she was to have her oldest daughter, her right-hand helper, home again. But the Least One had forgotten her! Tired as she was, that knowledge brought the tears to her eyes.

"Hit'll recollect ye again when ye frolic with hit," Mammy told her.

When she was fed, and sat warming herself before the hickory fire, Stacy Ellen put back her head and feasted her eyes on the circle around the hearth. Pappy, big and angular, Mammy, thin and tired-looking, Aaron, Fairannie, who had been named from a ballad song, the twins—a handful to manage—little Tom, and the Least One, whom they called Glory. Glory traveled from lap to lap, cooing, crowing, but avoiding Stacy Ellen. If only that provoking baby would not act so uppity!

Outside, the winter wind howled down Thunder Gap, but here, beside the fire, all was snug and safe. The fat pine crackled, glinting on red peppers and pumpkin that hung drying in the rafters. The patchwork on the poster bed looked gay, and so did the old, indigo-blue "kiver" Grannie had woven. Stacy Ellen thought how pretty the cabin would be, all decked with greens. She answered Mammy's and Pappy's questions about the school, and drowsy as she was, sang them the angels' song from the Christmas play. Then the Least One came creeping from lap to lap until she laughed up at Stacy Ellen, who took the plump little body into her arms.

"How about takin' yore thumb outen yore mouth?" she inquired after a while. The Least One looked at her reproachfully, but surrendered the choice morsel into her keeping.

Next morning the family arose from bed a good hour before the sun was up, and huddled, dressing, before the fire Pappy had made. From the kitchen shed came the sound of sizzling, and the aroma of bacon and coffee. Mammy had been up ahead of them, wrestling with the wood stove.

Stacy Ellen saw to it that the young-uns washed behind their ears; then she caught up the milk bucket and went out to the barnyard. From where she milked she watched Pappy disappear up the logging trail, driving the mule critter hitched to the wood sledge. "He's going after Christmas trees to haul to town," she thought, as the milk hissed against the tin bucket beneath her capable hands. "He'll haul 'em over the new road the Gov'-ment's building, and the money he'll get for the trees'll buy food to keep the folks till there's garden stuff in the spring o' the year. It'll pay my entrance fee back to school too." Even though Stacy Ellen worked her way in the school, Pappy had to help some.

"But there won't be money to spend on Christmas," she told the cow, "and it ain't our way to have a Christmas tree." No, Pap would never think to bring his own young-uns a Christmas tree. But why not have one anyway? She looked around, past the cow, to see if she could find one. Down by the creek was a whole thicket of holly trees, and before the cabin door grew a single holly, slim, pointed, and crimson with berries. "The very thing!" she murmured, "but there's nothin' for to trim it!"

The cow chewed her cud complacently as though to agree, "No, there's nothing for to trim it."

It was a beautiful tree, but the young-uns were used to it, and it ought to be decked somehow for Christmas. Stacy Ellen longed for tinsel, and an angel to go on its top, and colored balls to reflect happy children's faces, but these were out of the question. Her arms dropped to her sides and she sat on her little stool, staring out at the horizon. Then suddenly she awoke to the fact that the milk bucket was full to overflowing, and that the cow was looking around at her as though to inquire, "What more do you want?"

The next minute all thought of Christmas was banished from Stacy Ellen, for, as she entered the doorway with the brimming bucket, a chicken ran between her legs, tripping her. The twins laughed and she saved the milk by a miraculous feat of juggling.

"What's that chicken doing in the house?" she demanded, and the twins told her joyously that it laid an egg for them every morning on the trundle bed.

"The very idea! Well, I'll larn it better!" the older sister scolded, as she shooed the hen out the door.

The cabin was in confusion. From the kitchen shed came the "swish, swish," of Mammy's churn, and the young-uns were amusing themselves as they pleased. Aaron had let the fire go out, so that a patch of cold daylight fell down the chimney into the ashes. The peppers, which had caught the firelight last night, looked gray against the smoky rafters, the beds were unmade, and little Tom pulled about a chair, to which the Least One clung, staggering.

"I'm larnin' hit to walk," he announced.

"Well, don't pull so fast! Hit's legs'll give out," Stacy Ellen warned, feeling Christmas far, far away. She stepped out the door and drew a deep breath of the cold mountain air. Whatever could she do? Then she stepped in again.

"How'd ye like to deck this yere house for Christmas?"

The young-uns were puzzled. "How deck it?" they inquired.

"Oh, hang it with greens and suchlike."

Aaron looked dumbfounded. "They's some turnip greens in the garden," he told her doubtfully, "but they's froze."

"Holly and suchlike pretties!" she explained. And then the young-uns became interested and demanded to know more.

"If ye want to git ready for Christmas," she told them, "ye'll have to pitch in and clean up this shack within an inch o' its life—and, mind ye, it's got to shine before I tell ye any more about Christmas."

Immediately began such a scurrying to and fro that she had to stop them. "Wait!" she cried. "Aaron, you take out the ashes and lay the fire. Here, Fairannie, you sweep." She thrust a corn-shuck broom into the child's hand. "Tom, you kin mind the Least One, while one twin helps me make the beds, and t'other brings in kindlin' wood."

From that moment they were so busy that Mammy, when she came in from the kitchen shed, stood amazed at the order and cleanliness she beheld.

"Now," said Stacy Ellen to the row of young-uns, "we kin begin to think about Christmas. Aaron, ye kin knock to pieces yon old barrel in the barnyard, and bring me the wire hoops. The rest o' ye pull on yore coats and come with me."

Taking a knife, she went down to the holly thicket beside the creek and cut some beautiful twigs with berries, which she dropped into the hemp sack Fairannie held open. Next she led the young-uns up through the frozen cornfield, where, perched on the snake fence, she cut twigs from the slim, pointed cedar trees. Their berries were blue as the evening sky she had seen through the church house window. Last she gathered hemlock branches with cones like tiny, brown roses. All these she carried back to the cabin, and there, before the fire, she bound twig above twig on the wire hoop until, beneath her resin-stained fingers, lay a beautiful wreath. The young-uns watched, breathless with interest, handing her now a bit of holly, now a string to tie it, and now a cluster of cones. When the wreath was done, Stacy Ellen held it up.

"I orter have a red ribbon for it," she said critically.

"How'd a bunch o' my red peppers do?" Mammy inquired, for she had come in to admire.

"The very thing!" Stacy Ellen exclaimed, and when she had fastened the gay red in the green, she hung the wreath on the gun peg above the fireboard. The young-uns shouted with glee, for suddenly their cabin had become festive, gala, capable of any Christmas possibility.

Stacy Ellen left Fairannie and the twins making a second wreath while she took Aaron outside and talked to him confidentially.

"I want some pretties of some kind to deck this holly tree while the young-uns are asleep, night before Christmas," she told him. "Do ye reckon ye kin help me find some?"

Aaron wrinkled his freckled nose and then remembered that he had a treasure box hidden under the house.

"I 'low thar'll be something I could loan ye," he told his sister. "I have to keep the box hid so the young-uns won't finger my things."

With that, he dived out of sight and reappeared with a cigar box which, when opened, revealed eight feathers dropped by cardinal birds, six feathers from blue birds, and tiny feathers of the wild canary, some gay pebbles, and a roll of tinfoil.

Stacy Ellen clapped her hands. "Lawsy, Aaron," she exclaimed, "if ye'd picked these for a Christmas tree, ye couldn't a-done better! We'll stick the tail feathers in the branches and wrap the tinfoil around sycamore balls. They'll be a sight, a-hangin' in the holly tree!"

Snatching a hickory basket, she ran into the woods for the sycamore balls, followed by Aaron. They found the seedpods of teasel, also, and milkweed, and a dried branch of persimmon. It was amazing how much color you could find in winter fields and woods if you just kept your eyes open!

She and Aaron had filled their basket when they heard a crashing sound up in the timber. Rocks came rolling down the trail, underbrush was breaking. They looked at each other. Whatever could it be? Then suddenly the mule critter came galloping down the trail, dragging his harness behind him. Where was Pappy and the wood sledge?

"Whoa, Jonah!" yelled Aaron, and the mule critter drew up abruptly. He was trembling and wild-eyed. Something dreadful must have happened up on the mountain.

Stacy Ellen's heart sank, and Aaron went so pale that his freckles stood out starkly.

"We've got to go find Pap," Stacy Ellen murmured, trembling.

"I reckon ye're right!" said Aaron, and gathering up the reins, he turned the mule about. Leaving their basket and all thought of Christmas behind, they hurried up the mountain.

Strange, thought Stacy Ellen, that Jonah, the mule critter, always so greedy for food and stall at the end of the day, should now hurry back up the steep slope. Indeed, he went so fast that they had to stop him and climb on his back. Oh, whatever had happened to Pappy? They shouted for him at the top of their lungs, but the sighing of the wind in the trees high above them was their only answer. Stacy Ellen blinked back tears and Aaron bit his lips as they clung to Jonah's back. He carried them up and up, lunging over rocks and roots until he had passed out of the timber belt, and into the balsam pines that girdled the mountaintop. There, in a thicket, he stopped, and they jumped down and looked about.

It was cold up there. A light snow covered the ground and the green boughs of the balsams. Aaron and Stacy Ellen ran about, shouting for Pappy.

In the snow, they found the tracks of sledge runners, and following them, they discovered the sledge, overturned. It was loaded with Christmas trees which were tied with rope. Pappy had been ready to start down when something had happened. What was it—oh, what was it? Together they righted the sledge, shouting wildly.

"Be still, Aaron!" cried Stacy Ellen suddenly. "I thought I heard something that time." A groan came to her from beneath the ledge of rock where she stood. Fearfully they peered over it and saw Pappy lying with his foot jammed between two stones.

West Bend Comm Mem Library

This CHECK OUT RECEIPT
is the ONLY receipt you will
receive. Please KEEP it!

Title: Tales of Christmas from
near and far
Author: Wernecke, Herbert H.
(Herbert Henry), 1895-1975.
Item ID: 33357000319819
Date due: 1/8/2015,23:59

Title: Giovanni's light : the
story of a town where time
Author: Theroux, Phyllis.
Item ID: 33357002755333
Date due: 1/8/2015,23:59

Title: Family furnishings :
selected stories, 1995-2014
Author: Munro, Alice, 1931-
Item ID: 33357004658790
Date due: 12/26/2014,23:59

Title: New GMAT essentials
Author: Kaplan, Inc.
Item ID: 33357004360322
Date due: 1/8/2015,23:59

To RENEW by phone call
262-335-5151
Renew ONLINE with library
card and PIN at
www.west-bendlibrary.org
Click CATALOG/ACCOUNT
Then click LOG IN

"That ye, leetle gal?" he murmured feebly. "I 'lowed ye'd come! I slipped and a rock rolled on my foot. It's broke or sprained. Try—" But Pappy got no further. His eyes closed with the pain.

Stacy Ellen hardly knew how she and Aaron climbed down and dislodged the heavy boulder, but they did, and then came a greater difficulty. Pappy could not bear to have his foot touched. How could they ever get him up the sloping rock to the sledge? He solved the problem himself, easing his weight with one foot, holding to Stacy Ellen and Aaron with his arms, and dragging the injured foot. It was an agonizing process, but at last he reclined on the balsam bed made by rearranging the trees on the sledge. By the time Aaron had rehitched the mule, a faint smile came to his lips.

"Good old Jonah," he said to the animal. "I heerd ye break loose and overturn the sledge, but I didn't 'low ye had gumption enough to bring help!"

"Mules are smart critters though they be stubborn sometimes!" observed Aaron as they started their painful way down the rough trail. He walked, leading Jonah, while Stacy Ellen kept pace with the sledge, helping to support Pappy. It seemed to them that Jonah picked his way over roots and stones with extra care. After a long, long time they came to the cabin.

When Mammy had overcome her first fright, she took charge and they got Pappy into the house; then Aaron unhitched the mule and galloped away over the new road for the doctor. It was two hours before he could get there, but he reassured them after examining the foot. It was badly sprained and bruised, but not broken. Pappy would have to stay off it at least two weeks. When Mammy had paid the small fee the doctor asked, there was little left to jingle in the money box.

Stacy Ellen knew it was not pain that made Pappy look so unhappy now. It was worry, The sale of his trees in town would have brought money to keep them in food till the spring of the year, when he could work on the new road and make a garden. How could they get on, these worst months of winter, without that money?

"A body can't jest set still and take sich trouble!" she told herself, squaring her small chin. Then she burst out: "Pappy, why can't Aaron and I haul those trees to town? Ye could tell us what to do with 'em!"

Pappy looked at her hopelessly. They wouldn't know how to sell the trees, he said. No, he couldn't see their going.

"Ye needn't think I'm the homesick young-un ye took to school last fall, Pappy!" Stacy Ellen cried. "I'm full-growed now, and able to take keer o' myself. I jest know Aaron and I kin sell those trees."

Something about the look of her convinced Pappy. Hope came into his eyes, and he sat up, gazing at his daughter as though he saw her for the first time. "All right!" he said. "Go ahead and try!"

All at once it seemed to Stacy Ellen that the cabin was filled with Christmas. The scent of cedar in the fire warmth was part of it; and part of it was Mammy who was holding the Least One and suddenly began to sing an old Christmas ballad about Joseph, and a cherry tree that bowed down its branches so that Mary might pluck its fruit. The young-uns gathered round to listen. When the song was ended, Pappy glanced up and noticed the wreath for the first time. He complimented Stacy Ellen and remarked that town folks would like wreaths like that.

"Why not make some this evenin', an' take 'em along with the trees?" she suggested.

And that was how it happened that she and Aaron forgot how tired they were, and Pappy forgot his pain, making wreaths until the old clock on the fireboard struck midnight. It was a great stack of them that Stacy Ellen lifted out on the cold porch before they went to bed.

It snowed while they slept, and next morning, Stacy Ellen and Aaron had to shake the white from the trees before they re-loaded them in the jolt-wagon. A dozen beautiful wreaths they tucked between. Then, after Pappy had given last instructions, they flicked Jonah with the reins and drove away, crushing crystal grasses in the creek bed, tracking the snowy road to town. It was a long ride, but the cold, sunlit air was glorious, and town itself was a thrilling adventure. Perched on the high spring seat above their greenery, they looked down upon people, traffic, and dooryards, while the mule critter pulled them up one street and down another.

Success beyond their dreams awaited Stacy Ellen and Aaron. Because their trees were symmetrical and sturdy, people wanted them. And because the wreaths were unusual, as well as beautiful, they sold like hot cakes at a dollar apiece.

"I think we might take a leetle o' the wreath money," said Stacy Ellen at last, when the wagon was empty and the money box full, "and git some presents for the folks at home." So they bought a length of pretty calico for Mammy, a flashlight for Pappy, and a play toy for each of the young-uns. Stacy Ellen insisted that Aaron select the jackknife he had coveted so long, and they lingered with delight over the purchase of a small, woolly lamb for the Least One.

It seemed to them both that they had never been so happy as they were, driving home over the snowy mountains.

"There'll be the tree all trimmed when the young-uns open the door in the morning," Stacy Ellen told Aaron, blissfully. "Then we can make pull taffy and popcorn balls. And we'll ask Mammy to sing that cherry-tree song again about Mary and Joseph and the leetle Jesus. 'Pears like I never knew what a lovely song that were before. I'll take that back to the school! They favor sich old song ballads there, and put 'em in books!"

(MINNESOTA)

A Christmas Letter

GERTRUDE HANSON

My dear Jimmy:

The days are moving swiftly now toward Christmas—the third Christmas since we met, Jimmy. Do you realize that we have not yet spent this most festive of all the holiday seasons together? . . . But I mustn't dwell, as you so often remind me in your letters, on the thought of our separation. Instead I shall think of how we met at the ivy-draped chapel in my old hometown on the Florida coast; I shall recall the happy times we had together when you sang for the servicemen and I played your accompaniments; I shall remember to be glad because your parents wanted me here at your Minnesota farm home this Christmas; and I shall be grateful because I am able to render real service here while your courageous mother must spend months in the hospital. Most of all I shall remember those swift-flying weeks before you entered the maritime service—weeks that held the discovery of our mutual love, the miracle of our happiness when we decided to share our lives "for better or for worse. . . ." These are the offerings of frankincense and myrrh that I shall place on the altar of my Christmas memories—and I shall encircle them with my prayers for your safekeeping.

I am very thankful now because you kept on insisting that our letters must be complete and detailed diaries of our thoughts, hopes, and dreams, as well as a chronicle of all the everyday occurrences of our lives. That has kept us—whose lives are spent so differently now—from growing apart; and when you come back, we will meet as two who have shared all things together, won't we, Jimmy? Do you wonder why I write about some things several times? I do that purposely—for, of course, some of my letters may fail to reach you.

But the story I am going to tell you today about my baking experiences is one I could very well afford to omit altogether—for I'm certain that you'll hear much of it from every member of this household!

I may as well admit, right here and now, that it hasn't been all fun, this business of taking charge of the Norbeck household during your mother's absence. I've had to learn so many new ways—especially in regard to baking! . . . Almost as soon as I entered the door on the day of my arrival from the South, lovely, blond Karen said to me: "Do you know how to make *berlinerkranser*, *sandbakkelse*, *fattigmand*, *gorobrød*, and *rullepølse?* Mother always makes a lot of those before Christmas gets here." At six years Karen remembers things about Christmas that I never knew!

You can imagine how dumbfounded Karen's question made me, Jimmy. Why, I'd never even heard of those things—and when I admitted that (which I did, Jimmy, right there on the instant, believe it or not), your baby brother looked at me rather disgustedly and I heard him say, "Now I'm good and mad, and I'm going into my bedroom until I get over this!" Nels is positively the cutest little three-year-old I've ever set eyes on, and what he said made us all laugh so much that the ice of strangeness was broken. . . . Your father—whom I've loved from the beginning because he looks so much like you—tried to apologize, his strong countenance a bit flushed, his honest blue eyes a bit troubled. Rolf (he certainly is a strapping big fellow to be only seventeen) simply howled and shrieked with laughter; and Elsa, who for a girl of fifteen is so strangely gentle, considerate, and understanding, always, gave me a big hug and said, "Don't you worry about anything, Elizabeth. We're going to manage wonderfully well, you'll see!"

As for getting along together, we certainly have managed wonderfully, too—I'm quite helpless in my adoration of the whole family—but this foolish Southern-born and Southern-bred wife of yours hasn't gotten along well at all with the traditional Christmas baking!

A dear old lady, who lives over a mile away, brought us some mouthwatering *berlinerkranser* and *fattigmand*, and some of the other unpronounceable Norwegian cakes, one day. Of course I eagerly turned to her for help, but she, the darling old soul, had been making the goodies for such a long lifetime and in so many different ways that her "take a bit of this and a bit of that" directions did me very little good when I tried to follow them. You should have seen the results of my first attempts! The *sandbakkelse*, made in pretty little fluted tins; the *berlinerkranser*, which should have looked like miniature frosted wreaths; the rosettes, made on one of the baking irons kept in the old Norse chest, a lovely star-patterned design—all these took on the strangest forms for me, twisted, distorted concoctions that filled me with dismay and disappointment. When the children came home from school I was so nervously exhausted that Rolf said to me, "Why, Elizabeth, you're only a tiny jump ahead of a fit, aren't you!" He was closer to the truth than he realized. All I could think of was that the days were moving deep into December and I had failed to fill the empty containers with the customary Christmas goodies. The whole family—and I shall always love them for it—spoke kindly and encouragingly of my first attempts, but I knew very well that they were wondering what to do; and I knew that Christmas just wouldn't seem like Christmas without the traditional serving of Norwegian delicacies.

Then, a few days later—after I had tried the "a little of this and a little of that" method of making *berlinerkranser* again, without success—Mother Norbeck (bless her heart, and bless him who gave her the hint), from her hospital bed, sent me some rhymed recipes. She thought I might like to send them to Florida to my own mother, she said. That mother of yours, Jimmy, is not only the incarnation of courage but she is made up of unchangeable goodness and tact. . . . In almost feverish excitement I experimented with each recipe in turn—and good luck crowned every one of my efforts. . . . Well, you don't have any use for recipes, perhaps, but I do want you to see that your mother can write rhymes. . . . Rolf must have struck up an acquaintance, too, with the Muse, for one day, following a talk we had about Norwegian Christmas lore, he wrote this rhyme for me:

Do *julenisser* slip indoors
In happy Christmas fettle
And dip their little wooden spoons
Into the *fløtegrøt* kettle?

When Karen, coming in from school, saw my array of goodies, she went almost wild with joy. Nels went around with a beatific smile on his face. He was in the kitchen when I pulled the first pan of nicely shaped *sandbakkelse* from the oven, and he stood transfixed like one who has seen a miracle performed before his very eyes. . . . Elsa and Rolf, when they saw that I had the materials ready for making a *rullepølse*, insisted on helping me before they tackled their school studies. . . . When I showed the rhymed recipes to Daddy Norbeck, he laughed so heartily that the lines in his face, left there by long night hours of worrying about your mother's illness, seemed to disappear.

Maybe you can induce the ship's cook to try one of the recipes—and maybe you'll shed a few tears when you remember how deliciously your mother prepared these things. . . .

BERLINERKRANSER

Mix three egg yolks that have been boiled hard
(And please sing a merry tune)
With four egg yolks that have not been boiled
(And please use a wooden spoon).

Then take one cup of sugar—and blend
(Did you remember to sing?)
This sweetening with the well-mixed eggs
(A wooden spoon is the thing).

Take one full pound of butter that's soft
(Use substitutes this year)
And mix that well with flour—four cups
(Sing, cookie engineer).

Now alternate as you blend and stir
(And chill the dough overnight);
When ready to bake, knead out thin strips
(It's a Christmastime delight).

Make thin, tiny strips, and form into wreaths. . .
Whip an egg white, not too well;
Add sugar and frost each wreath. And you'll
Have cakes none can excel.

SANDBAKKELSE

Now here's a recipe that calls for one whole cup of butter.
The very thought of that would make my heart go flutter-flutter,
Until I learned that substitutes (say, half of margarine)
Will give the cakes a texture like the smoothest velveteen.

Work in a cup of sugar
Till it looks like angel fluff;
And add an egg. Be sure that you
First beat it well enough.
Now you take fifteen almonds and you shred them quite completely;
One spoon of almond extract, too, will flavor this discreetly.
Next, add some flour—for a soft dough; try two cups, more or less,
And you will have a batter filled with sweet deliciousness.
Use fluted tins for shaping
This small mouth-watering cake.
It's like a butter patty—and
It's liked for goodness' sake!

NOTA BENE: A fine addition to this recipe is three tablespoons of cream.

KJØDRUL OR RULLEPØLSE

If you want a treat that's noble, that is good beyond belief,
You should buy a five-pound mutton flank or, better still, buy beef.
Now flatten out the flank and split it into sheets, and then
Just cut your sheets in pieces that are—well, try twelve by ten.

Next, buy two pounds of veal in strips to lay on top of that.
(It will be just as good if you use pork that isn't fat!)
Now sprinkle all with condiments, a wide variety;
Use ginger, pepper, allspice, salt. Minced onions? Certainly!

Roll everything up well and tight—and sew and wind with string;
Place that in boiling water then and keep it simmering
Until the meat is tender. . . . When you cool it, use a press,
Or something heavy on it. This makes unmatched tastiness!

NOTA BENE: Serve cold, cut in thin slices. Some place the "*rul*" in salt brine a few days before it is boiled.

GORO

You have to use a special kind of iron
If you intend to make some *goro*-bread;
It's rich and wafer-thin, and all the Norskies
Who come from Norway have been *goro*-fed.

In times of scarcity we don't use butter.
  Instead we use two cups of good-grade lard;
Two cups of sugar, five eggs, some vanilla;
  And cardamom, or lemon isn't barred.

Now mix these things up in the usual manner
  And add two cups of thick, sweet whipping cream.
Believe me, you don't need to be Norwegian
  To know that *goro* merits high esteem!

In my spare moments, Jimmy, I am making samplers for our very own dining room—samplers of your mother's rhymed recipes. . . .

This year, Jimmy, will bring me my first white Christmas. As you know, I had not been away from the sunny South until I came here. All my Christmases have been green ones. Dear Jimmy, I know now why you spoke so feelingly of your Minnesota home, your northern winters, your Christmases. This far northern countryside lay snow-embroidered when I arrived in mid-November. Since then everything has been decked in bridal white, and there is a deep-settled, permanent look to this magic, winter-woven blanket of snow. The days are invigorating and exhilarating. Just think of it, I hadn't seen any snow, except in the movies, until my train reached your village early one morning! The change in climate hasn't troubled me at all. This isn't the winter-withered, cold-weary land that I thought awaited me.

Have I remembered to tell you that I always sit here at the dining-room table, in your very place and chair, when I write to you? Here, more than in any other room in this large and cozy home, I am able to catch the "feeling" of your family. . . . I had scarcely ever known anyone of Norse extraction until I met you, Jimmy! . . . In this room, which holds so many visible symbols of your family's background, the strange fabric of which my life is woven becomes intertwined with a cultural past that binds me to you and yours. . . . I look up from my letter-writing to admire the brightly decorated corner cupboards that are filled with treasured heirlooms of silver, brass, and pewter; the quaint Norse chest with its rounded top and its painted motif of gay flowers; and the beautiful hand-woven window draperies which are your mother's especial pride. Sometimes I get up to take a peek at the interesting contents of the chest—those priceless things which your paternal grandmother brought from Norway. On sunny days I move from the west to the south windows and look in wonderment at the diamondlike brilliancy, the almost blinding, crystalline glory of the out-of-doors—an experience that never fails to awe and stir me. If, as has happened several times, a cardinal settles himself on a nearby pine tree to serenade me with his bewitchingly lovely song, and a fairy shower of snow crystals falls as if to accompany the song—well, then the winter pageantry is likely to delay my letter-writing. But I know you would not want me to miss one single bit of your north country's winter beauty.

At home now (in Florida, I mean) Mother and Dad are making plans for Christmas too. I imagine I hear my mother suggesting duck with yams, or Bimini stone crabs (they're bigger and more delicate than any other variety, and I'm very fond of them); but Dad may be holding out for shrimp or Frogs' Legs Sauté Demi-Bordelaise.

All our thoughts center around Christmas now. I have the most exciting news! Your mother's doctor told me the other day that he is going to let her spend Christmas Eve and Christmas Day with us! Dear old Pastor Frithjofson and his charming wife are to be our guests on Christmas Eve—and they'll come early, bringing Mother. Oh, can't you visualize how contentedly Daddy Norbeck's eyes will shine and how hilariously happy even tall-growing Rolf and bright-shining Elsa will be? They all think we're going to leave for the hospital as soon as dinner is ended. Only one thing will not seem right—your empty place at the table—but I must not think of that. . . . The pastor has warned me that I must have plenty of *lutefisk* and oceans of melted butter sauce to go with the fish! . . . I have found it very easy to like *lutefisk*, since it is prepared on the same principle as our "down south" lye hominy, a favorite food of mine.

While I have been musing, Karen has come home from school. Elsa and Rolf will soon be here. I must not linger much longer at this writing, for there are recipes to try out for the evening meal!

Do you remember clearly what a December midafternoon is like on this farm, Jimmy, or have all the strange sights you've seen dimmed your remembrance? Someone (of course it was God, Jimmy) has painted long shadows of the trees on the unbroken snow. There is a pale, translucent glow from the early setting sun. The tall pines that fringe the hill slope to the south have put on cloaks of the color of night.

This may find you in tropic waters—or in the Arctic regions—but wherever you are, Jimmy, be sure of this—that I keep love's sweetness flowering in my heart's garden, and I eagerly await the hour of your returning. Good night . . . good night.

Your Elizabeth

P.S. Oh, Jimmy, your place at our Christmas table will not be empty! My dear, my dear! . . . I was ready to address this letter—and the telephone rang. The station agent in town called to relay your cablegram. . . . Your homecoming message is like a benediction laid over my deepest expectations. . . . Christmas at the Norbeck home will be a hallowed and unforgettable time. . . . God is good!

E.

(NEW ENGLAND)

On Christmas Day

MARGARET W. EGGLESTON

"DING, DONG. Ding, dong," sang the bell in the steeple of the tiny New England church on a Christmas Day many years ago. Down the road the villagers hurried, some in sleighs, some in ancient automobiles, and some on foot. It was to be a great day in that little church, for a junior choir had been formed, and was to march into the church for the first time, wearing the secondhand vestments sent by the pastor from a city church. Everyone wanted to be ready to smile at the children as they began that eventful march.

Enoch Dane and his wife, Sarah, were almost the last to arrive. They were usually late for service, but it was not because they were lazy or uninterested. Their hillside farm was more than four miles from the church, and they had no hired help to assist Enoch with the milking, or Sarah with her work in the big, rambling house. Sometimes they were late because Martha, their adopted daughter of eighteen, could not arrange her curls or her hat to suit her fancy. On this Sunday, however, Martha was already in the church when Enoch and Sarah arrived. Martha was to be the soloist of that junior choir; she was to lead the rest into the church.

Enoch Dane was a well-known character for miles around. His face, too often unshaved, was always a blanket of smiles. His ready wit and incessant stream of stories made him very good company. His generosity had kept the family poor in cash but wealthy in friends. Enoch was a pillar of the church. He sang in the adult choir; he took the collection; sometimes he even read the burial service for the dead. He tried his best to be a sincere, working Christian, yet he was a sore trial to Sarah, his wife, for he was easy-going, even shiftless, in his work on the farm. The barn door had hung on one hinge for three years. The end of the veranda, which had been added to the house ten years before, was still unfinished. Trees lay where they fell, even though good firewood was always needed in the house; grass often spoiled while waiting to be cut. "Haste makes waste," was Enoch's maxim, and his house and farm were a silent testimony to his lack of haste.

Enoch had inherited the farm from his ancestors. It stood on a high plateau, surrounded by higher hills on all sides. There was a lake a short distance through the woods, and Enoch often fished there. Sarah, being lame, could not walk that far; Martha was not allowed to swim or row, lest she be drowned. Enoch would listen to no arguments on that score. The farm was a place of great beauty and peace, but it was also a place of great loneliness and deprivation for the two women, Sarah and

Martha. The nearest neighbor was a mile away; no house could be seen in any direction. There were no labor-saving devices in the house, or on the farm, though the acres of giant pines could easily have secured them. Water had to be carried from a well, yet the hill behind the house had a spring which would have forced the water to the top floor of the farmhouse, if piped. Enoch just "didn't get at it."

Sarah Dane, to the stranger, was a very ordinary woman. She had never had a becoming hat or dress in the memory of the neighbors. She wore what was given her, regardless of style or color, and she never seemed to realize that she looked queer. Her hair was a bit curly, but it was always drawn tightly away from her face. The work on the farm was hard, and, being lame, it took Sarah long hours to keep the house as she wished to keep it. When she came to town, she usually looked as if she would like to "set and set," as Enoch often did, yet she was always busy at something.

Yes, Sarah was surely plain in looks, but her real beauty could not be hidden by homely hats or unbecoming dresses; sometimes they even enhanced it. Sincerity, nobility of character, and unfailing love were written in every line of her face. Sarah was the saint of the town, if there was one.

When a visiting artist sat behind her in church, he pulled at the sleeve of his friend during the hymn, saying:

"Man! Look at that face! I must paint it. One sees but one face like that in a lifetime. Introduce me to her. I want to ask her to sit for me." But Sarah had no time, nor desire, to have her portrait made.

As she limped painfully into the church that Christmas morning, she carried in her hand a bunch of red-velvet poinsettias, for Sarah liked to feel that she was making the house of God beautiful. All summer, flowers from her garden deluged the platform and pulpit of the church, though bending to weed them was always painful. She arranged her flowers, glanced to see that the chairs were in their places, and then reverently bowed her head to pray.

"God," she whispered, "I'm thankful for my home and for my church. Help me to spend this day in honor of the birthday of Jesus, my friend. Amen." Then Sarah read over the hymn, that she might sing it more thoughtfully later in the service.

Soon Enoch took his place in the small choir loft, his genial face appearing over the heads of the singers in the front row. He didn't pray; he didn't read the hymn; he just watched the door that led into the kitchen, eager to get the first glimpse of his Martha in her new vestment. When she walked through the door—her face reddened by the wind, and her pretty curls much awry—Enoch's face was a study in supreme satisfaction. Martha could sing well, and she knew it. Her voice rose above the rest of the choir, clear and sweet. Whatever Martha chose to do, she did well, and so she was a leader in the church and the community.

Martha was the child of Sarah's sister, who had died with pneumonia soon after the little one was born. Two years later the child had infantile paralysis, and then her shiftless father just disappeared, leaving the neighbors to do what they would with the baby. Inasmuch as Sarah was the nearest of kin, they sent the baby to her by a messenger. Years before, Enoch and Sarah had buried their only child, Benjamin, and Enoch's fatherly heart had yearned incessantly for another to love: so when Martha came—puny, helpless, sick, yet bright and beautiful—Enoch opened his heart and his home with a welcome that was deep and lasting. He had shared with Sarah the long, weary hours that had had to be spent, when farm work was waiting, rubbing the withered limbs. He had carried her about on his shoulders until she could walk again. Not once had he complained of the four-mile trip back and forth to school during the years. Enoch adored, and spoiled, Martha.

She had recovered from her illness in a remarkable way, but, to Enoch, she was always something to be spared, to be humored, and to be admired. So Martha, brilliant in school and active in the village, was lazy, selfish, and discontented on the farm. She wanted to go away to school. She was determined to be free to do as she chose, so she was a very real problem to patient, gentle, faithful Sarah.

On that beautiful Christmas morning, Sarah sincerely worshiped during the hour that she spent in the church; Enoch planned what he would do with Martha, and perhaps Sarah, for the rest of the day; Martha dreamed of what she hoped to do for the next few months or years, though apparently she was giving heart and mind to the singing of the old carols of the Christmas season.

Some of Martha's gifts had been in her stocking; most of them were waiting for her when she reached home from church. They ate a good dinner, enjoyed their gifts, and then Martha insisted that Sarah and Enoch should rest while she and Job washed the dishes. Job was a half-witted boy, the son of a neighbor, who was going to Texas the following day to live with a sister. He had come to say good-by to Martha and Enoch. At first, Sarah hesitated to leave the kitchen, but when Martha said that since she couldn't give them gifts, she wanted to serve them when she could, Enoch and Sarah left her with a smile of appreciation.

After fifteen minutes, Martha peeped into the living room. Both were sound asleep. Then Martha stole quietly up to her room, returning with two suitcases, both of which she handed to Job.

"They are asleep," she said. "Go quickly, and by the lower side of the house, where no one can see you. Put them out of sight in your barn under some hay."

When Enoch and Sarah joined her again, Martha played the old reed organ for them. She sang carols with Enoch and made maple candy for Job to eat on the train. All afternoon she was thoughtful and kind, and when the three went to bed, she kissed them good night, thanked them for her happy Christmas day, and for her many gifts. Sarah's heart was full of gratitude as she knelt by Enoch and listened to him pray.

"God, we thank thee for today. We thank thee for our home, and for Martha, who came to make us happy and glad. Help us to be grateful and true. Amen."

The next morning Martha was gone. Her old clothes were neatly folded in her bureau drawer. Her pretty red coat and hat, which Enoch had given her for Christmas, were not in the hall. Her violin had been taken from its place on the organ. In her haste to get away, she had spilled her box of powder on the living room floor, and one glove was on the snow in the yard.

On the dresser in her room Enoch had found a note, when he went to see why she did not come to breakfast. Speechless with fear and pain, he handed it to Sarah to read. It said:

> Dear Daddy and Mother:
>
> I want to learn to be a great singer. I hate the farm, and I cannot stay another day, especially since I now have a chance to go away. I wanted to say good-by to you, but I knew you wouldn't let me go if you knew my plans. Please forgive me for hurting you, but I have to go. Thanks for being good to me for so many years. I think I can take care of myself now. I am going with Job, so don't worry. I will write you someday when I know where I'm going to live. I have taken all the money that Mother left me ($10.87), so I have enough for a long time. A kiss for both of you, and good-by.
>
> Martha.

After Sarah had put the letter down on the table, Enoch read it again; then he walked to the stove, tore it slowly into very small bits and dropped them into the coals, a few at a time. For a moment he looked dumbly into the face of Sarah, and she put her hand lovingly on his bent shoulders, though she spoke no word. He walked, as if in a daze, to his bedroom and shut and locked the door. When he came out, ten hours later, Enoch looked haggard and worn. His face, usually so happy and covered with smiles, was bitter and set in ugly lines.

"Sarah," he said, decisively, "Christmas and God and Martha have all gone out of my life together. I have learned that none of them are worth what they cost. Never mention any of them to me again. Remember."

Sarah silently nodded her head and kept on with her work. Enoch might keep her from talking, but not from loving and forgiving. She knew that she wanted and needed God and Martha and Christmas in her life, even more than before.

Five years went by—dreadful years for Enoch and Sarah. His form was bent; his hair turned white; his words were few and bitter. Sarah's soul seemed seared with his cruelty, and she worked harder and harder, that she might have less time to think. She looked tired and worn and discouraged. One letter had come from Martha, but Enoch had returned it unopened, not even letting Sarah know its postmark. Occasionally word came to them of Job, but Martha's name was never linked with his, and the villagers did not know they had gone away together. Knowing the heredity of Job's family, Sarah's heart was sick when she thought of the fate that might await Martha's children.

At first, Sarah had hidden away all of Martha's things; then, one by one, she had given them away, lest Enoch find them and be angry with her. Each Christmas she had made a little box of seed cakes, such as Martha had always expected to find in her stocking, and she had secretly bought a present or two. Christmas was just like any other day in the farmhouse after Martha went. It was lonely and full of regrets. Sometimes Sarah would steal into the parlor and have a good cry as she looked at the picture that Martha loved best, *The First Robin of Spring*, and when she went to bed, it was always with a prayer on her lips for Martha. Sarah suffered in silence, yet in faith.

The old car had literally fallen apart, so each Sunday, Sarah rode alone to church in a wagon that had been used by Enoch's ancestors, and behind an old horse that seemed about ready to follow the example of the car. Church was even more lonely than home, yet Sarah went; she tried to do her share of the church work, and also Enoch's. Sarah's religion was her comfort and challenge; Enoch's was his goad and his torture.

Then Christmas came again on Sunday. The snow was deep, and Sarah found it difficult to get to church. While she was away, Enoch swept the barn, moved some hay from the loft, oiled the harness, and did many other things that could have waited for Monday. He ate his dinner in silence, but as he rose he bent and kissed Sarah, in lieu of a Christmas present. Then Sarah was glad. A kiss had been a rare thing since Martha had gone. Sarah knew there must still be love in his heart and that he must be remembering the day.

After dinner a terrible snowstorm came up the valley, and the wind sent great drifts of snow swirling about the farmhouse. Enoch walked to the window many times and looked out. Sarah knew that he was restless and unhappy, but she did not know how to help. At last, toward evening, he put on his great sheepskin coat and fur cap. He took his snowshoes from the peg, and made ready to go out.

"Don't wait up for me, Sarah," he said. "I'm going to walk—miles, maybe; maybe only rods. You're a good wife, Sarah, better than I deserve. God must love you, even if he hates me—and Martha."

Sarah started. It was the first time he had ever mentioned Martha's name. She kissed him gently on his forehead and took his hand in hers.

"Enoch," she said, "God loves you—and Martha too. I love you both, and I can forgive you both, even though you have both been stubborn and unkind. God forgives and loves, even more than I."

It seemed as though he were about to speak. He opened the door, and shut it again. He looked at her intently, while his hands fumbled with his fur cap; then he shook his head sadly, and went out into the storm. Sarah feared for his life, for she knew he was tired and worn. She lighted a lamp and put it in the east window, so that it might light his way back if he found the going too hard. Later she put one into the west window, for she didn't know which way he had gone. She made a blazing fire in the fireplace that it might seem cozy when he came in. After two hours she made a pot of coffee and a plate of cinnamon toast. Enoch would surely be hungry.

Enoch went slowly up the hill at first. It was hard going, but he pressed on until he came to a queer, old house where his grandfather had lived when Enoch was a little boy. Creeping into the lee of the house, he got out of the fury of the storm, and he stood there for a while. Through the darkness, he saw the light in the east window.

"No wonder Martha couldn't stay there when she was eighteen," he said to himself. "I should have seen it. That place is too lonesome for a girl. Maybe it is too lonesome for Sarah too." He pushed his way over the crest of the hill when the wind dropped a bit.

"I should have let her go to school," he said. "I was selfish; I wanted her all to myself. I should have let her have some boyfriends, too, but I was afraid she would go and leave me alone again, just as little Benjamin did. Oh, Martha! Why did you go?" he cried, passionately. He went on, passing the farmhouse where Job had lived; then he clenched his hands.

"A half-witted man for a husband," he muttered, "when I wanted her to have the best in the county." In the distance he could see the spire of the church, for the snow had ceased to fall, and the moon was peeping out. Enoch felt impelled to go in that direction.

"I haven't been there since the day she sang her solo. My, how proud I was of her that day!" he said. "The church is always unlocked. Maybe I will go down there and sit for a while. Sarah seems to find courage there. Maybe Sarah is right when she says God has forgiven us both. I'm sorry I have been so unkind to Sarah. She looked old today. Sarah is a good woman."

As he rounded a curve in the road, pushing steadily ahead on his snowshoes, he saw a woman trying to make her way in the drifted road. She was carrying a bundle in her arms.

"There's Mrs. Banks out in this storm," said Enoch, moving far to the side of the road, lest she call to him and want to talk to him. "Even a storm like this can't keep her from going to see her mother."

There was a cry of pain; then with a sob the woman fell headlong into the snow, her bundle rolling into the bank before her. Enoch turned quickly to help her to her feet.

"Daddy! Oh, Daddy, weren't you going to speak to me?" cried a weak, trembling voice. "Forgive me, Daddy. I had to come home to you this Christmas Day. See! I have brought you something." She tried to lift the bundle, but her strength had been used in her struggle against the storm. Enoch gave the bundle to her as she sat in the snow.

"See, Daddy," she pleaded, "I have brought little Enoch to you. He needs a father, Daddy. His father is—" but she could not say the awful word. She put her head down on her baby, and cried as if her heart would break.

Enoch stood as one transfixed. Martha had come home! What could he do? He bent and pushed aside the blanket that covered the face of the baby. It reminded him of Martha when they brought her to him—motherless, fatherless, sick, and needing a good daddy. The little child smiled at him, but Enoch turned away from the two.

"Daddy!" cried the young mother, as she saw what he had done, "for Jesus' sake, forgive me. It is Christmas Day. I have done no wrong since I went away. Enoch's father was a good man, and you would have liked him. I wrote to tell you where I was, so that you could come to see him before I married him. He is dead, Daddy! Dead! I am all alone. I want to see Mother, and have her love me, and kiss me good night. I want to sleep in my little bed. I want you to love me and little Enoch. I want to know how to make my baby grow to be like you."

Enoch winced at her words. Like him? God forbid. He had been a demon for six years.

"And Job?" he asked, in a husky voice.

"Job?" repeated Martha. "I know nothing of Job. He only took me to Portland in his old car, so that I could get a train. Job tried to persuade me not to go, and he tried to get me to come back to you when he went on to Texas, as soon as we got to Portland. Job has done you no wrong, Daddy."

A great load seemed to be lifted from Enoch's shoulders as he listened to what she had to say, and as he looked longer into her tired, honest, loving, hungry eyes. He raised her gently from the snow, and folded her close in his great arms, while the child cried quietly at her feet. Soon he picked the baby up from the ground and rolled it tightly in the blanket. Unstrapping his snowshoes, he fastened them to Martha's feet.

"Come, child," he said tenderly, "let us take the baby and go home. It is your home, and the baby's home, for always. Let's go to Sarah. She has never ceased to look for you, Martha. How glad she will be!"

Holding the baby close in his strong arms, he strode before her, eager now to get back to the comfort of the farmhouse.

"See, Daddy," she cried happily, as they came to the crest of the hill. "See! There is a light in the east window. Mother is watching for you."

"And for you, Martha," he said, stopping to kiss her again.

"And will Mother forgive me, and welcome the baby?" asked Martha, anxiously looking up into his face.

"This morning Mother said to me, 'I love you both, and can forgive you both, even though you have both been stubborn and unkind,' " said Enoch. "Mother has much to forgive, but her eyes will shine and her arms will be open when she sees you and your baby come back again."

Sarah was watching, and even before they reached the door she had flung it wide open, and had reached out her hands for Martha's bundle.

"Welcome home, child," she said, though she had asked no questions. "You have brought me a Christmas present, and I am glad."

Enoch waited until Martha was sitting before the glowing fire with little Enoch on her lap, eating Sarah's cinnamon toast. Then he lifted Sarah's face to his, kissed her tenderly, and whispered: "Forgive me, Sarah. I am sorry. Thank God, we have Martha in our home for Christmas."

"Martha—and God—and Christmas," said Sarah, as she browned more toast. "Martha, and God, and Christmas have all come to this house to stay."

(NEW ENGLAND)

A Puritan Christmas

LOIS LENSKI

"WHAT? Not keep Christmas?" asked Aunt Charity. "As I'm a God-fearing woman, what's this new world a-coming to?"

"No, we keep it not," said Goodwife Partridge, her sister, sadly. "Life hath been hard with us these ten years. It hath taken all our time and strength to feed and clothe our bodies—we've had none left for jollity."

"So sad-faced and dour you've all become!" Charity went

on. "The moment I stepped ashore I thought you must all be a-mourning for summat, your countenances looked so heavy and sad. The childer—haven't they . . ."

Goodwife Partridge looked about at the little faces—at Seaborn, ten, the eldest boy, at the two girls, Comfort and Submit, aged eight and seven, and at the two littlest boys, Waitstill, five, and God-be-thanked, three. She shook her head sadly as she spoke.

"Seaborn was born on the ocean before we set foot on this strange soil and the others were born here in the new country. They know not the meaning of the word 'Christmas.' The Governor, the Parson, and Magistrate say 'tis wrong. They say we came here for work and not for jollity."

" 'Tis time you heard it then, childer sweet!" laughed Aunt Charity. "Your aunt hath come over the ocean to tell you of Christmas, sweet Christmas!"

"Oh, tell us, do tell us, Aunt!" they begged.

"When thou hast been here for ten long years, thou wilt no longer laugh and tell merry tales," said Goodwife Partridge in a low voice.

" 'Tis time you heard of life in Old England, where mirth and jollity still reign, where life is not so stern. Dear Lord, may I never forget, no matter how old I grow. When the Christmastime comes in Old England, dear-my-loves, 'tis the time when Jack Frost takes us all by the nose, so we make shift to rub out the winter's cold by the fireside. 'Tis then the great Yule log is put on the fire, stories are told, and songs are sung. And all the little boys and girls have puddings with raisins in them and minced pyes and Yule cakes rich and sweet . . ."

"But is it not wicked, Aunt?" asked Seaborn, pondering thoughtfully. "Parson Humphrey would say that such things are an abomination of heathendom and the ruination of souls."

"But oh, what fun!" cried Comfort, her eyes sparkling. "I should have liked it, had I been there."

Aunt Charity sat down on the bench by the fireplace and the children crowded close on the floor about her feet. To hear this aunt, their mother's youngest sister, but just come over from England with strange words in her mouth, was a strong temptation indeed, but what a pleasant one. Such tales as hers had never met their ears before, nor set their hearts so eagerly fluttering.

"First all the pewter and brass is polished so bright, it shineth like the sun indoors!" Aunt Charity's sweet voice went on. "The servants are washed and dressed in prettiest bib and tucker and here and there they run, as smug as new-licked puppies. For into the Great Hall all the Master's tenants and neighbors soon foregather, to drink of his good ale, into which toasted Yule cakes are soaked and softened. The Yule candles are already alight when the merrymaking mummers come to shout:

" 'A merry Christmas and a happy New Year,
Your pockets full of money and your cellar full of cheer!' "

"Sister!" interrupted Goodwife Partridge severely. "Why remind us all of things which have gone past, never more to return? Dost wish to breed discontent? Here we have more solemn things to engage the mind—work, the shortness of life, the swift coming of death. I want not the children's heads befuddled. See how bright their eyes do shine, like in a feverish sickness, when one lieth at death's door!"

"Hush! Speak not of death!" Aunt Charity looked down at the children. "They are alive for the first time in years. 'Tis the first happiness they have known. The mere telling doth give them pleasure, their little lives have been so dark and drab, so starved. . . . Yes, you have spent time and strength to feed and clothe their bodies, but their souls you have forgot." She went on with her story. "The bouncing log on the chimney hearth doth glow like the cheeks of a country milkmaid. All the spits are sparkling, for the hackin—a great sausage—must be boiled by daybreak. . . ."

A man suddenly entered the low-ceiled room. "Hackin! Hackin!" he cried sternly. "Who speaks of hackin here?"

"I tell the sweet childer of Christmastime in Old England, brother-in-the-law John!" answered Charity.

"Christmastime in Old England!" said Gaffer Partridge sadly.

"Is there still such a thing? I had forgot. I had forgot. Christmas! To think it still goes on as it did when I was young and ran about in pinafores. Here we have no time or place for such goings-on, but it can do no harm for the childer to know what once it was."

"Oh, husband!" cried Goodwife Partridge in alarm. "Hast lost thy wits? How canst thou see thy children's heads befuddled by wild tales?"

Gaffer Partridge seemed not to hear his wife's words. He sat down heavily on the settle and stared into the fire. He spoke as if to himself alone: "I came but now from the meeting place. There saw I Goody Nichols chained to a post for scolding her man in a loud, harsh voice. William Muddleton was set in the pillory in the marketplace for idleness; and at the whipping post yonder, Daniel Joslyn laid the cat-o'-nine-tails on a poor wretch's back, the while his cries did rend the air. Here, in this new land, we seem to think of naught else but wrongdoing. I like it not. Mirth and jollity we have forgotten quite. Is this the good life that we came so far to find?"

"Oh, Father!" cried the lass, Comfort, running to his knee. "Did you keep Christmas, too, when you were small like me?"

Gaffer Partridge turned away his head. The tears rolled down his cheeks one by one.

At daybreak on the twenty-fifth of December, two days later, no sound of caroling or of chimes broke the morning quiet. Now and then a chill breeze blew inward from the sea, bringing scattering gusts of snow. One by one, the chimneys of the low, thatch-roofed cottages began to show thin trails of smoke. Without, in the harbor, the frail ship, *Fearless*, rocked back and forth on the waves, worn out and battered after her long voyage across the Atlantic.

Through the narrow, winding streets, on which a few months before the town cows had made their slow and patient way to pasture, walked a little girl with woolen shawl wrapped tight about her head and shoulders. It was Comfort Partridge. In her cold, unmittened hand she carried a pail half-filled with fresh, froth-covered milk. As she hastened along toward her home, her little cowhide shoes made a sharp patter on the hard, frostbitten ground. Suddenly she stood still and bent her ear to listen.

A man, stoop-shouldered and bent, came along the path. He carried a bell in his hand, which he rang noisily. Then in the pause which followed, he cried out: "No Christmas! No Christmas!"

Christmas! All of Aunt Charity's words came tumbling back into the child's mind. She stood still and thoughtful, scarce heeding the little group of people who gathered to hear the Town Crier's words:

"Market to be held as usual . . . shops must be opened for folk to buy . . . farmers to yoke their ploughs, townsmen to raise the new dwellings, and women to spin in their doorways where they may be seen. A day of work and no cheer . . . a day of work and no cheer . . . by order of the Governor of the colony . . . to be enforced by the Magistrates . . ."

The listening people tightened their lips and went on their way. Comfort shivered with the cold. A tear rolled slowly down her cheek. She grasped her pail more tightly and hastened home.

The heavy batten door swung slowly shut behind her. She put down her pail, removed her shawl, and hung it on a wooden peg. Then she approached the table where the family waited—her parents and aunt seated on wooden stools and the children standing.

"Thou'rt late, child!" reproved Goodwife Partridge. "What delayed thee?"

"I stood for a moment . . . to listen to the Crier," answered Comfort. She pressed her white cap more firmly over her wayward curls, then straightened her white kerchief and apron. "The Crier said"—her thin voice pierced the heavy silence—" 'at Christmas is a day of work and no cheer." Her blue lips trembled.

"And so 'tis!" echoed her mother. Then more sharply: "Hast forgot thy message? Did'st inquire about Neighbor Minching and his sick wife? She's better—Goodwife Minching?"

Comfort Partridge shifted from one foot to the other. She was a responsible child. She had not lived her eight years in vain—eight years in learning not to forget.

"No, Ma'am, I forgot not," she replied slowly. "Goodwife Minching's taken a turn for the worse and Endurance is come down with the sickness too. And their cow is most dry. This—'tis all the milk could be spared. Neighbor Minching asked if you and Aunt Charity could come and care for her, since Endurance must also keep to her bed."

" 'In the midst of life we are in death!' " Goodwife Partridge gave her sister a meaningful look. As soon as the porridge was eaten and the table board cleared, the two women left the house for their neighbor's. No one in the little seaport town ever called on a neighbor in vain. Then their father left, too, to help with the raising of a new pine cottage, one of the many being rapidly built for the newcomers from the *Fearless*. And so the children were left alone.

It was when Comfort and Submit were scrubbing the table board that they remembered.

"Just so do they do in Old England to make ready for the Christmas feast," said Comfort, thoughtfully. "Aunt Charity said the board is always scrubbed till it shines as white as new-fallen snow."

"I wish we lived in Old England," said Submit, biting her little red lip.

" 'Tis here we can worship God as we please," said Seaborn seriously. Being the eldest and a boy, he felt heavy upon his shoulders the responsibility of the younger ones. " 'Twas for that very reason our parents came across the sea."

It seemed strange to hear the sound of children's voices. When their elders were present, they knew well to hold their peace and listen respectfully, speaking only when spoken to. Only when the elders were absent did their bright voices rise and fall freely like the piping of happy birds.

"I've seen the laurel and ground pine and hemlock greens a-growing in the woods," cried little Waitstill. "We need not go to Old England for them. They grow right here, even as our fuel grows at our very doors. We could fill our arms to overflowing . . ."

"Why, so we could, my lambie!" answered Comfort, her eyes suddenly aglow. "Seaborn, let us keep Christmas just for ourselves this day—while the elders are away. 'Twill be a little play of our own and can do no harm. I mind all the things sweet Aunt Charity did tell . . ."

Seaborn shook his head. "Parson Humphrey said that such things are an abomination . . ."

The door opened, and Aunt Charity walked in.

"Your mother can do all that's needful for Goodwife Minching and her daughter," she announced. "She was worried for fear God-be-thanked might fall into the fire and be burned or you'd forget to fetch wood enough and let the fire go out, so I thought it best to come."

"Oh, Aunt Charity!" cried Comfort, her face shining with eagerness. "How good of you to come! We thought to keep Christmas this day, whether the Magistrate says so or no . . . just for ourselves at home . . ."

"Christmas! Good Yule!" said Aunt Charity softly. "I never thought I'd live to see it in this hard, cold, righteous land—but mayhap I will!"

"There's Silence Pitkin—she's always sad and never talks or smiles," ventured Submit timidly. "She would like Christmas, I know full well."

"And Preserved Rogers," added Waitstill. "He never plays stool-ball for fear the Magistrate might pass and see him."

"And Temperance Seward," added Comfort, speaking boldly now, "who always talks of death and thinks each day her last. We'll make things ready—the Yule log, a great feast, the Christmas greens—and bid them all welcome!"

"None of the other children know about Christmas," said Submit softly. "They have no sweet Aunt Charity to tell them."

" 'Tis time they knew," said her aunt. Her words were short, but a smile played on her lips. She set to work with a will and all the children helped.

"But what if the Magistrate comes?" asked Seaborn, over and over again.

At midday, when sad-faced Silence Pitkin and timid Preserved Rogers and solemn Temperance Seward and other little boys and girls came to the Partridge home, they saw many surprising things. They saw Christmas greens, laurel, hemlock, and ground pine wreathing the batten door and embowering the fireplace. They all helped drag the Yule log in to the hearth, the girls first washing their hands at Aunt Charity's behest, in order, according to the old belief, to make the fire burn more brightly. They saw the shining table board set with a feast, and they ate heartily thereof—roast meats and codfish and mackerel, besides stewed pumpkin, beans and parsnips, and honey and maple sugar for sweets.

Afterward came the games, blind man's buff, puss in the corner, hot cockles, forfeits, shoeing the mare, and hoop and hide. Aunt Charity taught them all and none were slow in learning except three-year-old God-be-thanked, who managed always to get in the way of the others, and Silence Pitkin, who had sometimes to sit down for lack of breath, so unaccustomed was she to the playing of games.

Then Aunt Charity taught them a lusty carol, and they all sang together as they had not been known to sing in all their solemn lives:

" 'Lo, now is come the joyful'st feast!
 Let every man be jolly,
Each room with ivy leaves is drest,
 And every post with holly.
Now all our neighbors' chimneys smoke,
 And Christmas blocks are burning;
Their ovens they with baked meats choke,
 And all their spits are turning.
Without the door let sorrow lie,
 And if, for cold, it hap to die,
We'll bury 't in a Christmas pye,
 And evermore be merry!' "

As the little voices rang out happily, Comfort noticed that her father and mother had returned and were standing back in the shadows watching. Then Preserved Rogers saw his parents and Silence Pitkin hers and before anyone realized what had happened, the Partridge house was filled to overflowing with its neighbors. The carol was sung over and over again and all the people smiled as they listened.

Suddenly a loud knock was heard on the batten door. The song died away, and the children ran to their parents.

"What meaneth this frumpery?" A man's voice sounded in loud, cruel tones. Everyone knew it was the Magistrate. His face was dark and flushed with anger as into the low-ceiled room he strode.

"What meaneth this?" he cried, pointing with his wooden cane. "What mean these greens about this hearth encircled?"

Little Waitstill had not lived long enough—but five years only—to learn that man can change a beautiful world into a sour one of his own making. In his innocence, he thought the strange, dark man had come not to berate, but to admire. He clapped his little hands eagerly. "Oh, good sir!" he cried. "We found all the greens a-growing at our very doors. Dost not rejoice to see them? It seemeth as if the summer's sun hath changed the earth's white-furred gown into a gay, green mantle! Doth it not?"

"Hush, hush!" cried Goodwife Partridge in affright.

"Take the child with his noisy prattle away! Heard I not but now loud sounds of joyous singing and of mirth?" the Magistrate went on. "Methinks 'twas not the singing of holy psalms!"

He bent his head and with his long nose, sniffed hither and yon. "What odor greets my nostril? Smell I not sweet cakes, cakes made from forbidden sweetening and baked for Yule?"

The people fell back, and not a word was said in reply.

"Ah! Ye need not speak. Me ye cannot deceive." Angrily he pulled open the door of the Dutch oven still resting among the warm ashes on the hearth. "Baking Yule cakes—is that wherewith ye women waste your time? There . . ." but no, the oven was empty. "Ye've given them to the childer . . ." He looked, but he saw not a mouth that chewed, not a jaw that moved.

Only little God-be-thanked whimpered under the stern gaze. Then the child's hand darted, swift as a bird, to his mouth and something was popped inside.

"There! A Yule cake! The child hath a Yule cake! Open thy jaws! Show me the cake!"

In a flash God-be-thanked gulped once, then a second time, and the cake was gone. Obediently he opened his mouth and there on his fat red tongue, a telltale line of white crumbs did show, which but angered the Magistrate the more.

He turned to the elders.

"Men!" he cried. "Where are thy tools? What hast thou done with ax, knife, auger, pit saw, frow? Why be ye not at work? Know ye not we must build new homes for the newcomers from the *Fearless?*"

"Our tools are gone to be mended this day, good sir," spoke up one of their number.

"Women!" the Magistrate went on. "Why are thy spinning wheels idle? This is a day of work and no cheer."

"We have no flax, good sir," spoke up one of their number. "We cannot spin without flax."

"No tools! No flax!" snorted the Magistrate. He looked round the room, and his eye lighted on the table board, from which the food and tranchers and pewter had been removed. It shone bright and white in the flickering firelight. "There! The shining board! That proveth there hath been Christmas-keeping here! The shining board . . ."

His eye lingered on it, and as Aunt Charity watched him, she thought to herself that his face softened a little. Perhaps he, too, remembered Christmas in Old England, though he dared not confess it. Now, now was the time to speak. So Aunt Charity stepped bravely forth and told the Magistrate that it was she who had helped the children—the little children who had never known what Christmas was—to keep it.

" 'Tis the day of the Lord's birth!" she added softly. "He came to lighten men's hearts. In Old England, 'tis a day of joy and cheer. Joy and cheer are needed in this New England even as in the Old."

The Magistrate listened in amazement, and as he listened, his frown grew heavier.

"Thou art frank, Mistress, and brave-spoken," he said. "Thou art new to this land, having but so recently stepped ashore from the *Fearless.* As time passes, thou wilt learn that our ways are not Old England's ways. We left them behind us to make a better life for ourselves here. Our law reads: Whosoever shall be found observing any such day as Christmas or the like, either by forbearing of labor, feasting, or in any other way, shall be fined five shillings or be imprisoned. The edict is, work or go to the gaol. Work or go to the gaol—male or female. But we suspend sentence this once, since thou art a newcomer. See thou, however, that it doth not happen again."

He stalked out the batten door. On the sill he turned. "Gaffer Partridge!" he called. "Remove this frumpery at once. See that this foolishness doth not happen again." He poked his wooden cane in the greens over the door and pulled them roughly down.

"Yes, good sir!" "Rightly, good sir!" "Thank 'ee, good sir!" obediently answered Gaffer Partridge and his neighbors.

The door closed and the Magistrate was gone. The men and women set to work at once pulling down the Christmas greens. While they worked, they looked at each other and smiled. "We kept Christmas once again—and with our childer too!" There was a light in their eyes which had not been there before.

Aunt Charity gathered the group of children about her and sat down on the settle.

"Was it wrong, then, after all?" asked Seaborn, the eldest.

"Oh, no!" answered Waitstill. "The greens were so beautiful to see!"

"And Silence Pitkin smiled again and again!" added Comfort. "She was happy for the first time in her life."

"And Preserved Rogers played games so lustily!" Waitstill went on. "We never thought he could play at all."

"And Temperance Partridge spoke not once of dying!" added Submit, happily. "She asked if she could come back tomorrow!"

"And God-be-thanked swallowed the last Yule cake in the nick of time!" said Aunt Charity, with a laugh. "Well, dear-my-loves," she went on, as the tears filled her eyes, "ye've kept Christmas for one time only! Now hearken well—that which ye have in your hearts can never be taken away!"

"Christmas! Christmas!" echoed the children. "We've kept Christmas!"

"And ye'll never forget, will ye?" asked Aunt Charity.

"No, sweet Aunt!" answered the children. "Never shall we forget. That which we have in our hearts can never be taken away!"

(PENNSYLVANIA)

An Amish Christmas

ELLA MAIE SEYFERT

"HE'S TENDER! He fattens long enough, and I think he eats good," said Mother, proud of her success at turkey-raising. She was going over the eighteen-pound bird carefully for the last time, getting him ready for the Christmas feast the next day.

Martha and David crowded about closely as Mother flipped the breastbone once more, wiped the big turkey both inside and out, and then looked again to be sure that every pinfeather was out.

The whole house was aglow with Christmas! Hetty had given it a special cleaning, washed the windows, scrubbed the porches, and even scalloped papers for the closet shelves! Mother's luscious fruitcake, all tied up in a white muslin cloth and looking like a bad case of toothache, had been mellowing in a big, brown lard can for over a month. She had made her springerles, pfeffernuesse, kuchen (cakes), mince pies, and souse (pig's feet jelly) the day before, and now everything was ready for the great day.

Martha and David had watched all these preparations with delight. But as usual, Martha showed her excitement more than did David, and asked a hundred questions, squealing and hopping about in glee.

"Looks like the wedding," she said, pinching one of the turkey's cold, plump legs. "Look! How big they make! Maybe the *Belsnickle* comes tonight, Mother, not?" she asked with high hope.

David had been telling Martha again about the German custom of boys calling themselves "Belsnickles," going from house to house on Christmas Eve with their faces masked, throwing candy and nuts on the floor for the children to pick up.

"Then when the children try to pick up these goodies," he told her earnestly, "the Belsnickles try to switch their fingers. Afterward, they hand the switch to the mother, who puts it on the mantel to use during the year if the children are bad."

"Or, maybe the *Grishtkindl* comes?" Martha asked now, thinking he would be gentler than the Belsnickles. "The Grishtkindl brings the presents with his reindeer. But only to good girls and boys," she added. "David says so, Mother."

But Mother and Father did not talk much about such things. They believed that Christmas was the day when the "inner light" shone bright on everyone and the true story of the Christchild should be told instead.

"Martha," said Mother, "run upstairs and bring down the long, brown-paper bundle tied with red string. It's on top of my painted chest."

Martha found four other packages on the painted chest too, but she picked out the long one tied with red string and carried it down the stairs to Mother.

"O-oh! Such fluffy, woolly slippers!" she exclaimed, when Mother opened the bundle.

"There," Mother said, smiling, as she handed a pair of lamb's wool slippers to Martha, "put them beside Grandpappy's bed tonight when he sleeps. Then he thinks the Grishtkindl was here."

Martha thought this over quietly for several seconds. Then she slipped her hands into the warm lamb's wool and looked at Mother knowingly. "He fools himself, but he likes it, not, Mother?"

"Christmas gift! Christmas gift!" Martha called over to David's room the next morning bright and early.

"Christmas gift! Christmas gift!" David answered her, and then there was a race to see who would be downstairs first.

"Christmas gift!" Mother greeted them, and handed each one a round, brown-paper package.

In David's package was a red *wammus* and a big penknife. And Martha received a shiny school box with three bright-colored lead pencils inside, and a box of very pretty *schnoop-duffs* (handkerchiefs).

"Hetty and I make the dinner today," Mother reminded Father when breakfast was over. "It's a long way to church, over to the Beilers'—so make yourself ready, David. You go to church with Father today."

"It snows! It snows!" Martha was calling from the "best room," where she was trying out her new colored pencils. "Mebbe the Grishtkindl brings his reindeer, David!"

"Well, you tell him I'm a good boy, Martha, if he comes—I go to church."

"Maybe you bring somebody back from church for dinner," Mother suggested to Father. "Sammy Fasnacht likes to eat, or the Kreider sisters—they live all alone. It's a big turkey, you know."

The snow became deeper and deeper all morning, and Martha kept wiping the steam from the kitchen windows with her bare hand, for every time Mother opened the oven door to see if the sizzling, sputtering turkey was browning properly, a puff of steam would blow out and cover the cold panes. Martha wanted to see down the road. The Grishtkindl might come!

The "best room" was cozy and warm. Baby Jacob sat on a thick blanket spread on the floor near the stove, and Martha played with him.

"It's Christmas, Jacob, Christmas!" she said, bubbling over with joy. "See your new horsie! David gives him to you. Look! He has a shiny harness, just like Cap, and his tail is plaited with red string!" But in answer baby Jacob only tried to stuff his calabash rattle down his throat as he gurgled and cooed.

"Church must make out now sure," Martha thought aloud, trying to see through the "best room" windows this time.

"Oh, they come! They come! Church makes out!" she called joyfully to Mother, who was busy whipping up the mashed potatoes that were to be served with the creamed onions, corn, coleslaw, turnips, and all the "fixings" of the turkey.

"A big car comes too! Iss it the Grishtkindl, you think, Mother?" Martha asked excitedly.

Mother took another look at the turkey and then slammed the oven door shut before running to the window to see for herself. With one swipe of her apron, she cleaned the windowpane of steam. Yes, Martha was right! Father's yellow Germantown wagon was almost at the gate, and right behind it was a big, gray trailer. Mother knew! She had seen trailers when she drove to Lancaster.

"It's the house on wheels—I see them in Lancaster once, Martha."

"Hetty, come," Martha squealed, beside herself now with excitement.

Hetty ran across the kitchen floor and the three of them, Mother, Martha, and Hetty, crowded close to the window. Mother had to keep wiping the steam from the panes as they watched.

Cap stopped at the gate. The wheels of the wagon were clogged with snow and the top looked like a big, white-iced cake. Father and David got out just as the trailer drew up in back of them, and a man stepped out of the automobile part. Then Father and the strange man, with David helping, broke a path up the snow-covered walk to the door of the "best room."

"Mebbe the Grishtkindl sends him!" Martha insisted, still hopeful.

"Mother," Father said, as he opened the door and stamped his feet to shake off the snow, "they buy some milk of us for their Christmas dinner. We have some?"

"Some milk!" she exclaimed, too surprised to say more as she followed Father into the kitchen.

David and the strange man, who was tall and beardless, crossed the room to stand by the stove. Baby Jacob, surprised by the stranger, started to cry and David picked him up to comfort him. Martha had forgotten all about baby Jacob, she was so curious about the house on wheels. She still had her face pressed against the cold windowpane, looking out through the storm at another little-girl face pressed tightly against the small trailer window. Martha could hardly believe what she saw!

"Maybe they would eat Christmas dinner with us." Mother found words at last, turning to Father in the kitchen. "The turkey is done and it is plenty. Sammy Fasnacht doesn't come—*nein?*"

"*Nein*, he has it so in his back." Then he said, "Ya, vell, I ask dis man," and Father went back to the "best room" again.

"Well," said the strange man, whom David and Martha afterward always called "Mr. Trailer," "my wife had dinner about ready, but it certainly would be fine to have Christmas dinner with a real family in a real house, and it is certainly good of you to invite us."

"Ya, vell, iss goot," said Father, as Mother rushed out to the kitchen to set three more places at the table.

So in another minute Mr. Trailer was going back down the snowy walk, and before long the side door of the trailer opened and a pair of steps unfolded and dropped to the ground. Then a little girl about Martha's size hopped out, followed by a woman. They had coats thrown over their heads, and while the man closed the door of the trailer, the little girl and her mother waded up the drifted path and into the "best room."

As Mother took their coats, Mrs. Trailer looked about the pleasant room and drew nearer the stove. "It's so cheerful and warm in here!" she said. "Thank you so very much for asking us!"

Martha watched Mrs. Trailer and the little girl shyly for a few minutes before going nearer. She thought Mrs. Trailer was almost as nice-looking as Mother, and the dress the little girl was wearing was as pretty as those the Brooks twins had on the day she went to school with David.

Mother gave all the coats to David, who hung them in a row on the wall hooks. Then he hurried over to Grandpappy's room to help him to the window so that he could see the trailer too.

"*Du liever friede!* [Did you ever!] It makes me think of the old Conestoga wagons they had for hauling when I was a boy, before we had trains." Grandpappy was so excited he had to go over to the "best room" to see the strangers, and David led him. There he talked with Father and Mr. Trailer, telling them all about the old times, when they drove eight horses hitched to the old Conestoga wagons.

"Eight horses to pull the heavy loads over the mountains," he said. "And the bells that hung over the horses' collars made like chimes. We could hear them far over the valley. Times change! Ya, vell—" And after this long speech Grandpappy tottered back to his room again to wait for dinner.

While the men talked, Mother and Hetty were busy in the kitchen, putting the finishing touches to the Christmas feast. Mrs. Trailer played with baby Jacob, and Martha entertained the little girl with her dolly, Sally Ann.

"*Kann er Deutsch?* [Can you talk German?]" she asked, handing Sally Ann over to her little visitor.

"I'm Victoria," the little girl replied pleasantly, for she thought that Martha had asked her name.

"What?" Martha asked.

"Victoria is my name. What's yours?"

"Martha. Martha Wenger."

"That's a pretty name," said Victoria. "Let's play school, shall we?"

"Yes," Martha agreed. "And first we sing "Beautiful Snow"—like at my school," she said in her grown-up way. "You know, mebbe my little schoolhouse comes down and then I go to a big school. But I like my little school besser."

Victoria didn't know what to say to this. She thought a big school much more exciting. Most little girls wanted to go to a big school.

"Why do you have tucks all around your waist and sleeves and at the bottom of your dress?" she asked, looking Martha over carefully.

"It's to let out when I grow, see?" Martha showed her where Mother had already ripped out a tuck and the material was much brighter. "Pop says I grow like a weed!"

At this they both giggled, and their giggles tinkled across the room like tiny bells, only to be silenced by Hetty calling them to dinner.

"Look," said Martha, stopping in front of Victoria before they went into the kitchen. She pushed at a loose front tooth with her tongue. "It wiggles—I must eat slow."

How nice the table looked! Right in the middle of it Hetty had placed a tall glass like a vase, filled with green celery. The tumblers held red-fringed napkins folded three-cornered, and Martha was delighted to see that the turkey reposed on the big purply meat platter that had a peacock painted in the center.

The long quiet blessing seemed extra long to the hungry children, who eyed the steaming turkey over their noses. Mother held baby Jacob on her lap and had to keep pushing her plate out of reach of his clutching hands.

At last Father stood up and carved the turkey! And he did not have to count for his "seven sours and seven sweets" today. There they all were in front of him!

"Help yourself! Help yourself!" he said again and again. "Mother grows this turkey—it's a fine bird."

"Yes, it is," agreed Mr. Trailer. "But we raise good turkeys in Canada too."

"You are from Canada, then?" Father and Mother both asked at the same time.

"Many of our Amish people live in Canada now," Father told him.

"Yes," answered Mr. Trailer, "we live in Canada. Now we are on our way to Florida for the winter—but we started a little late!"

"Indeed we did," said Mrs. Trailer, "because this is a part of the country I should like to drive through in the summertime. Your Lancaster County farms must be beautiful. Such fine barns and houses!"

"Fine indeed," agreed Mr. Trailer. "No wonder Lancaster County is called the 'Garden Spot of America.' And I hear that you are going to build a big schoolhouse near here soon."

At this Martha stopped chewing and sat with her fork raised in the air, while David held on to a turkey leg with both hands. It was a serious moment. Father crossed his knife and fork slowly on his plate before he spoke.

He won't be joking now, thought David.

"Ya-a!" Father began. "We have our little red schoolhouses for many years and now the Government tries to do away with them and build one big schoolhouse where all the children go together!"

"That is the new idea in education," Mr. Trailer assured Father. "The township school, they call it."

"But," Father argued, "the people must borrow the money to build the big school. That is needless—to borrow. Our Amish people don't believe that way. Besides, we want our little one-room schools near our homes. Then our children can walk there, and needn't ride by a bus, *nein!*"

There was a silence now, broken only by a squeal from baby Jacob banging his pudgy hand on Mother's plate. Martha lowered her fork and David started to eat the turkey leg. Father thought a long time before he spoke again.

Then: "It's shust like this," he went on. "Our Amish people are not well known, and we are not proud and worldly. We keep to the old ways in everysing, and we want our children to do the same."

"I see, I see," said Mr. Trailer, realizing how serious Father was.

"We must keep our little schoolhouses," Father spoke again, "so our boys and girls will grow up in the way we think is right!"

After this he passed the mince pie around the table so that everyone could help himself. Then Christmas dinner was over!

"Look, Victoria, my tooth still sticks!" Martha showed her on their way back to play.

"Why don't you pull it out?" Victoria suggested, very brave as long as it was not her tooth.

"Huh-uh!" Martha objected, shaking her head. "It falls out mebbe when I don't know it. Grandpappy tells me when der Grosspappy was a little boy, long ago, the blacksmith pulled teeth. But he don't pull mine!"

Just then Victoria's mother called to her. "We must go now," she said, and both little girls looked unhappy over the parting. "Thank everybody for such a delicious Christmas dinner, Victoria."

Mr. Trailer wanted to pay for their dinner.

But, "*Nein, nein,*" Father refused him, looking at Mother, who agreed with him with a nod of her head.

"We help spread the 'inner light' today," she said quietly over baby Jacob sleeping peacefully in her arms. "We have plenty. And maybe you stop again when you come back!"

Mr. and Mrs. Trailer smiled and thanked them again as they moved toward the door.

Martha was off in a corner of the room, looking over her new box of handkerchiefs.

"Dis one," she said to herself. "Dis one with the tulip worked on it—it's prettiest." Then to Victoria: "Here," she said, "you have a pretty *schnoopduff* for church. I play the Grishtkindl fetched it!"

"Thank you very much, Martha, it's lovely." Then Victoria stepped out into the snow behind her father and mother, and soon two happy little-girl faces were again pressed flat against icy windowpanes, gazing out at each other until the trailer disappeared in the falling snow.

The day after Christmas, which the Amish people call "Second Christmas," turned out to be fine and clear. The snow had blown and drifted high on the byroad leading out to the State Road, and Father and Mr. Hurst and David were opening it up. Martha watched them for a few minutes from her bedroom window. They were shoveling what were called "turnouts" where the snow was piled high on both sides of the road. Drivers had to stop and look ahead; then one would wait while the other, going in the opposite direction, would pass.

Soon the delicious, familiar smell of funnel cakes reached Martha and sent her scurrying to the kitchen for her breakfast. Hetty had already made a stack of the buttered funnel cakes, which she was keeping warm in the oven while she went on baking more.

She would let the batter run out of the blue funnel onto the sizzling hot plate, closing the bottom of the funnel with her finger while she moved it to another part of the hot plate. Then she turned the cakes deftly with a queer-looking paddle that Grandpappy had made out of iron a long time ago. It had a paddle on one end and a fork on the other. Father joked about it sometimes, saying, "It is like a good rule—it works both ways."

Breakfast was late this morning because Father and David had gone right out to clear a path through the snow in the by-road, and Hetty was keeping the funnel cakes warm for them. Baby Jacob was an early bird this morning and Martha, after stopping to watch Hetty for a second, ran over to hug him.

"Hetty makes funnel cakes for us this morning, Jacob. You must make big quick so that you can eat some too." Then, clapping her hands, she sang to Baby Jacob:

> "'*Botsche, botsche, kuche,*
> *Der baker hot gerufe*
> *Wer will goot kuche bache,*
> *Er muss haven sieben sache.*'"
>
> (Paddy, paddy the cakes,
> The baker has called
> Who wishes to bake good cakes,
> Must have seven good things in them.)

Baby Jacob was clapping his hands too, and then suddenly he burst out laughing—and no wonder! For Martha had backed right into a bag of Mother's rag-carpet balls and had fallen, rolling over and over on the floor, while Tommy, the cat, who hardly ever left the barn to come into the house, was scampering wildly across the kitchen toward Martha.

"My tooth's out!—It's out!" Martha shrieked weakly. "Where iss it, though?" She jumped up and stuck her tongue through the empty space to make sure it was really gone. Then she looked all over the floor. When she noticed Tommy, he was gracefully arched, ready to pounce on something.

"Tommy—it's mine! Here!" And Martha snatched the pearly tooth swiftly from under his soft paws and clutched it tightly in her fist.

"I drop it down a rat hole, Tommy," she told him. "Out in your barn. It gives a gold tooth then. Hetty tells me so!"

She ran to the window and saw Shep gamboling about and

barking at the bright, drifting bits of snow as the men shoveled.

Soon Father and David started toward the house, and Martha ran to help Hetty get the chairs to the table for breakfast.

Later, when the snow had settled enough, Father decided they would go sleighing. "We take Mother to the store in New Holland," he told Martha, who had been coaxing for a sleigh ride all morning. So after dinner he went to the barn to take out the old yellow sleigh that had stood so long in the wagon shed without being used. Its runners were rusty and rough, and the red, plush-covered seat was white with cobwebs and dry straws. It had not been out of the shed for two whole years now because Grandpappy's pink goose bone had not given any snows all last winter.

The sleigh looked very queer to Martha. She watched Father from her usual place at the kitchen window, while he brushed it carefully before hitching Cap into the shafts.

"Br-r!" Father came stamping into the house to put on his long, heavy coat. It had a shoulder cape, just like the kind of cape the Pilgrims used to wear. The coat looked green from age, but it was good and warm and Father would wear it a long time.

"Dress warm, Mother—*iss kalt!*" he said as he carried Grandpappy's brown buffalo robe from the back of the "best room" settle out to the sleigh. He covered the seat to make it warm for Mother and Martha. Only Mother and Martha were going with Father, and they tied blue veils over their bonnets to keep out the cold air. Martha sat between Father and Mother. Though she stretched her short legs as far as she could, she could barely reach the brick that Mother had heated in the oven and Father had put on the floor of the sleigh to be sure their feet would keep warm. After Father tucked the blankets all snugly about them, they were ready to start.

From the porch where they stood to wave good-by, Hetty and David could see Cap plant his feet firmly as he strained on the shiny, screechy harness that Father had bought for him at the Menno Weaver sale. The sleigh creaked as it slid along the first few feet of snow with a jerk. Martha thought the floor boards were being twisted and torn apart as she saw the shafts wiggle sideways with every pull. She looked into Father's face, expecting him to tell them to get out of the sleigh.

But he did not. Instead he said: "It goes better when the runners wear smooth awhile. Soon you have to hold your bonnets! Giddap, Cap!"

And sure enough, they were going faster and faster now. The sleigh runners sang a merry tune as they slid ever more smoothly over the crunching snow. Father had no bells on Cap or on the sleigh. Bells were "of the world," he thought, and against his religion. Besides, the sleigh could be seen very easily in the daytime against the white snow. But at night he always had a light, because that was the law.

Twice on the way to New Holland Father stopped the sleigh and got out to knock the big balls of snow from Cap's hoofs. It had packed so hard on all of them that he looked as if he were running on stilts. And Father thought he might slip and fall, and perhaps break a leg. He would never want this to happen to Cap.

As they rounded a long curve, still some distance from the town, Martha could see away off a long, covered Conestoga bridge across the Conestoga Creek. She wondered how Cap would ever manage to pull them through it, because there wouldn't be any snow in the bridge. But Cap knew what to do. He pulled the sleigh up the little hill and stopped just at the entrance to the bridge. Then Father got out and, after handing the lines to Mother, he pushed with all his strength at the back of the sleigh.

E-e-e-sh-e-e-sh! The sleigh scratched and scraped over the dry, loose boards of the bridge. E-e-e-sh-sh-e-sh! Mother shivered at the squeaky sounds. "I'm glad it's over," she said, when she handed the lines back to Father.

"Not so bad when we come home. Other sleighs and automobiles carry snow in and make a track for us, Mother!" Father said comfortingly.

When at last they drew up in front of the grocery store in New Holland, Cap was frothing around his harness and steaming in the cold air like a basin of hot water. So Father threw Cap's own blanket over him to keep him from catching cold.

Then they hurried into the store. Once inside, Martha clumped round and round in her heavy-soled shoes, looking at everything as she tried to warm her numb feet.

But now she soon forgot all about her feet in her interest in the store. "It's the Grishtkindl all around!" she whispered to Mother. "I like it! He looks so kind—just like the Bishop!"

Mother had not brought eggs today, as she very often did, to trade in for sugar, coffee, flour, rice, or macaroni, because the hens did not lay as well when the weather was cold, and too, she had used so many eggs to bake her Christmas kuchen!

"Now, some peppermints for Grandpappy," she said to the clerk after all her groceries had been bought.

"You have one now, Martha. Grandpappy would say so!"

Martha took one of the shiny, red-striped candies and popped it into her mouth as she followed Father and Mother out to the sleigh. All the bags of groceries were dropped under the lid of the seat, and they bundled themselves in once more. The sleigh creaked and groaned again as they started off with a jerk, and soon the whizzing, singing sound of the runners was music in Martha's ears. She did not wear her veil going home, and the biting wind stung her cheeks until they were rosy as a pippin apple. The peppermint candy, which was tucked away in her right cheek, made her mouth feel cold inside too. Sometimes the wind got up under her bonnet and almost lifted it off her head. But she would pull it on again and then cover her hands quickly under the blanket.

"Our Martha sleeps tight tonight!" Father was sure when he lifted her out of the sleigh in front of their own blue gate. "She's no *penesick maid* [sickly girl] mit such red cheeks. Look—David and baby Jacob hammer at the window, Martha!"

"Tomorrow mebbe we take baby Jacob for a ride, not?" Martha begged of Mother.

"Ya, vell, mebbe," Mother agreed, "if the wind lets up."

(PENNSYLVANIA)

The Christmas Candle

CHARLES STRYKER INGERMAN

THE AIR in the shed was heavy with the smell of bayberry. Becky, standing beside Mom, said: "It sure smells good, ain't?" Mom's big hand dipped the wicks in the deep pot of cooling wax, and when she lifted them, the row of fattening gray-green candles dangled side by side. "You have right," Mom answered. "A little girl I know, also, who thought picking bayberries was too much work, ain't?"

Pop Weyerhaus and Mom and Becky and the three boys were Pennsylvania Dutch. The first Weyerhaus had come to Pennsylvania from Germany long before the Revolutionary War. He and his neighbors had built the big stone farmhouse where a great many Weyerhauses had been born. And after all those years, Becky and her family still spoke a strange language, part English but mostly German.

"Mom," Becky asked, leaning nearer, "could I make a candle too?"

Mom hung the finished candles on a hand-whittled rack to cool and harden. "Yes," she said, "this year, you can make the Christmas candle." She smiled. "You like that, huh?" Becky's blue eyes shone with happiness, and she nodded eagerly.

Mom took a length of the flossy candlewick, twisted it tight, and tied it to the wooden handle. Becky began to dip it. Into the wax, and then out in the air above the pot until the outside had cooled. In and out, slowly, and each time the candle got bigger.

"Slow but sure," Mom said. "And it must go all the way to the bottom each time, see? Otherwise the candle grows loppity."

"Pop says that the Christmas candle burning in a window brings the Christ-child," Becky said slowly. "Is it true, Mom?"

Mom went on redding the candle-making equipment in the shed. "It might be better to say," she explained, "that the

Christmas candle burning in the window means the family in the house is ready to welcome the Christ-child."

"Hm-m-m-m!" Becky mused in a wise, ten-year-old manner. "But does he sometimes come, Mom? *Wirklich?* Really?"

"They say so," Mom replied cautiously. "Ask your Pop. Pop is smart. Could be he knows for sure."

She gathered the last pots together. "Are you finished with the Christmas candle yet?"

"Just now," Becky answered, holding the gracefully tapered candle in the air.

"Good," Mom said. "We will wrap each one prettily. Then tomorrow we'll go with old Chimmy to the town, to leave them in Elias Eisenhammer's store for the people who want real bayberry Christmas candles."

"And can I go with?" Becky asked.

"Well, ya," Mom answered. "If you don't be a *schlussel* with your work, you can to the town with."

Next morning—the day before Christmas—was clear and cold. A new blanket of snow had fallen during the night. Becky, looking out of the kitchen window while she was helping Mom with the breakfast dishes, said: "It looks exactly like the world was made fresh this morning, Mom!"

Pop was busy cutting firewood with Amos Bleimuller between morning and evening chores. The boys had gone with him. There were always plenty of things for boys to do, and Pop said children should learn to work young.

Becky hummed happily as she helped make the beds and redd the house. Then, after she and Mom finished an early lunch and had put the shining dishes back in the painted cupboard again, they hitched the venerable horse, Jimmy, and started out. Becky was wide-eyed with excitement, for it was always fun to go to the town. She was curious about the people who wore worldly dress, not like her own plain clothes. She was always intrigued by the shopwindows full of "boughten" things.

Mom left the candles in Elias Eisenhammer's store. Becky stayed very close to her. The town seemed terribly big and strange.

"Do we go home right away?" Becky asked as they left the store.

"Well, now," Mom said with a puzzled expression, "it wonders me what to say."

"What's the matter, Mom?"

"Elias Eisenhammer says Cousin Hannah is not so good. And the children are not so good too."

"Should we go help?" Becky asked.

"I should go help," Mom agreed. "But I don't want you to come along."

"Why not?" Becky queried. "I can help good too, Mom."

"You're a good helper, all right, Becky," Mom said. "But the children have measles. Ach, measles at Christmastime! It wouldn't be so smart for you to catch them too. Or the boys."

"No," Becky agreed. They'd never had measles at the farm, and Becky didn't want to have to stay in bed with the curtains drawn shut as her friend, Miriam Langbaum, had had to do.

"So," Mom said slowly, "it makes a problem for me." She still wore the puzzled expression. "Where could I leave you, Becky, while I go see how it is by Cousin Hannah?"

Becky thought hard. "With Elias Eisenhammer in the store?"

"Elias is too busy today to have a little girl under his feet."

"Could I stay at the stable with Chimmy?"

"No," Mom objected, "stables are no place for little girls."

"Could I sit in the train station and watch the trains and all the people?"

"Well," pondered Mom, "could be that would be all right. You'd stay right there and be a good girl for Mom?"

"Yes," Becky promised.

"Come then," Mom said. "I'll put you in a good place to watch and wait. You'll stay right there till I come back again?"

"Yes, Mom."

Becky sat in the station where Mom had left her. Several persons smiled as they passed, seeing her sitting there primly, her hands folded in her lap, wearing her long, plain-people clothing and her apron and her little black bonnet.

If passersby thought her quaint and sweet, she thought them strange and wonderful. "Such bright dresses!" Becky whispered to herself. "Such hustle and bustle! And how unhappy so many of them look!"

Becky thought the soldier looked especially unhappy. He had been in the telephone booth, and it had been easy to hear the anger in his voice as he spoke loudly into the telephone. Now he came out, and his face was flushed, and he was muttering to himself. He flopped down onto the bench beside Becky, and he exclaimed: "Now, doesn't that take the cake?"

Becky wasn't sure he was talking to her, but she was the only person near him. "What?" she asked sympathetically.

The soldier didn't turn toward her. He just sat there on the bench, sort of slumped, and the way his face was twisted, he looked like one of Becky's little brothers about to burst into a storm of tears. Even if he seemed old enough to start raising a beard, like Hennery Stoltzfus.

"You'd think they would tell a guy," the soldier said in an angry voice.

"What?" Becky asked again. "What didn't they tell you?"

"I came home on leave—a two-day Christmas leave—" the soldier muttered, "and the folks have gone off visiting relatives in the West."

"You didn't tell them you were coming?"

"I didn't know," the soldier said. "I just thought they'd be home at Christmas. I thought it would be a great surprise." He paused, and the hurt-little-boy look came back to his face again. "Now I don't know what to do, or where to go, or anything."

"How about uncles or cousins or relatives?" Becky asked.

"No good," the soldier said disconsolately. "I haven't any kin around here. Just Mother and Dad."

Becky was thunderstruck. It had never occurred to her—amply provided with kinfolk—that anyone could be otherwise. She sat there, hands still clasped sedately in her lap, looking at the soldier, who had propped his chin in his cupped hands and was staring sourly into blank space.

It was then that the Great Idea came to Becky.

"Why don't you come to my house for Christmas?"

He turned and looked at her for the first time. "Say," he exclaimed, "I'm sorry to be popping off like this. Why"—with wonder in his eyes—"you're just a little kid, aren't you?"

"I'm ten," Becky answered.

"I thought you were a little old woman," the soldier said. "I really did."

"Would you like to spend your Christmas leave with us?" Becky repeated. "There's just Pop and Mom and the three boys and me—"

"No, little lady," the soldier replied, "I guess—"

"You just go down the South Road two miles," Becky explained. "You take the first left-hand crossroad. We are the second farm on the right. The name on the mailbox is Weyerhaus."

The soldier suddenly had to blow his nose. "Maybe your Mom and Pop—"

"They'd be very glad," Becky said with conviction.

"Well," the soldier said, "I'll see." He got up slowly. "I got to get some lunch. Thanks for letting me cry on your shoulder."

"You didn't!" Becky objected.

"I almost did," the soldier laughed. "Good-by, little lady."

"Good-by," Becky answered.

She was still sitting there, hands in lap, causing a gentle smile now and then, being a good girl as she'd promised, when Mom came back.

And as they jogged home, Becky listened to Mom's story of Cousin Hannah and the children. But she didn't say a single word about the soldier who almost cried and the Great Idea. . . .

Pop had come in from the barn. He was scrubbing his strong hands and arms with lots of soap. The boys were already washed and combed and waiting for supper. Night had fallen, and large fluffy flakes of snow were drifting against the panes of the window.

All the time she had been helping Mom fix supper, Becky had been thinking about the Great Idea. She was a little worried. Would the soldier come? And especially, what would Pop say if he did come? Becky knew how bitterly Pop was opposed to war.

"Isn't it time?" Becky asked anxiously. "Isn't it time to light the Christmas candle, Pop?"

"Right away now," Pop replied, laughing and drying his hands. "An extra place set at the table, too?"

"Yes," Becky answered.

"Well, bring the candle and a match," Pop said.

Becky already had them in her hand. Pop took them, lighted the candle, let a little of the sweet-smelling wax drip on the windowsill. There it was, burning in the window, a beacon for the Christ-child. Everyone was still, and Pop said slowly:

"Dear Jesus, this is to let thee know that thou art ever welcome in this our house."

Pop turned toward the table, loaded with things good to eat. "Come," he said. "I am very hungry."

Becky had her nose pressed against the windowpane. "Wait, Pop!" she called, and there was a world of excitement in her voice. "A light shows in the lane!"

Pop turned, came back to the window, peered out. "Ya," he agreed, "you have right. Someone is coming."

A car drew up into the yard, and a car door slammed. A second later, someone was knocking at the kitchen door, right beside the window where the Christmas candle was burning.

Pop opened up. Becky's eyes were shining like sparks. For there, in the doorway, was the soldier!

"I suppose I shouldn't have come, really," the soldier was saying. "The cab is still waiting if I'm intruding. But I was so downright blue and unhappy, and the little girl said—"

"Tell the cabdriver we were expecting you," Pop ordered in his deep, beautiful voice. "And come in."

Pop was not mad. Pop was as nice as pie, and Mom was as nice as pie, and the boys were almost out of this world with excitement. Becky could have hugged herself with joy.

And he was the nicest soldier. Of course, he didn't speak good Pennsylvania Dutch. But he did speak a kind of German, and that was easier for all of them than English.

"No, thank you," he said to Mom. "I couldn't eat another bit. Really, I've eaten enough for a company now." And he laughed his nice laugh that showed his white teeth.

"I must go out to the barn," Pop said, "to see if everything is all right by the animals."

"May I go along?" the soldier asked. "It's been a long time since I smelled the inside of a barn."

Becky watched Pop nod, and she felt a glow of pride in her father and in her soldier.

When they came back from the barn, they were chatting like old friends. Becky was clearing the table. Mom was upstairs, shushing the boys to bed.

"You're sure it'll be all right if I help you in the morning with the milking?" the soldier asked.

"Sure," answered Pop. "Glad to have you."

And later, when Becky was kneeling beside her little old bed, she whispered: "Oh, thank thee, Lord Jesus, for Christmas and Pop and Mom and the boys and my soldier."

She was just turning down the covers when she heard feet in the hall. The door opened, and there stood Pop and Mom.

"You're a good girl, Becky," Pop said.

Becky felt warm and happy. She got into bed and Pop tucked the quilts under her chin. "Pop," she asked, "Pop, you think maybe the Christ-child sent us the soldier?"

Pop stroked his black beard, and there was a happy, faraway look in his gentle blue eyes. "Could be, yet," Pop said gravely. "Could be maybe the Christ-child sent him."

(POLISH-AMERICAN)

The Pelaski Children's Christmas

ETTA W. SCHLICHTER

DUCKS TO ROAST for Christmas and a great mince pie from the baker's!

All the Pelaski children wanted a real American Christmas such as their schoolmates in the big city were planning. They had been born in Poland—Anton and Moritz, Edouard and

Marcelline. Only the little Clara was a real American, named for a lady whose picture Mother had seen.

But they were all Americans at heart. Only their mother sometimes grew homesick for Poland and told them stories of when she was a child there.

"We might have a Polish Christmas," she said one day. "Then you could see how we did in the old home."

"No, sir!" said Moritz, clenching his fists. "We don't want any old Polish Christmas. We're Americans now."

"It's a great deal better here," said Anton. "Father says so. We have the big school to go to and baseball—"

"Ah, baseball," jeered Moritz. "You think you can play baseball, but you can't. I could do better myself if those school guys would let me be on the team."

"I'd like to see you," said Anton angrily. "And say! I'd like to know who took my roller skates. Did you, Ed?"

"No," said Edouard, but he looked guilty.

"You did, too, and you can just take that," said Anton, giving him a kick.

"Mother," cried Marcelline, "just look at my clean dress. Clara put her sticky fingers on it and made a big chocolate spot. I'll slap you for that, missy." And Marcelline, before her mother could stop her, boxed little Clara's ears.

"You're a mean old thing," screamed Clara, "and I don't like you."

"Crosspatch, crosspatch!" teased Edouard, pinching Clara's ear till she shrieked again and tried to kick him on the shins.

"Hi, hi!" cried Mrs. Pelaski. "This is a fine way to behave the very day before Christmas. You may put the fat candle in the window and the lights on the Christmas tree, but why should the Christ-child want to come to a home where there is quarreling and angry words with kicks and blows?"

The children were silent and very much ashamed.

"Tomorrow," said Mrs. Pelaski, "we have a Polish Christmas. That will teach you to behave."

"Oh, no, Mother," cried Edouard and Marcelline. "We want an American Christmas."

"A real Polish Christmas you cannot have," said Mrs. Pelaski sadly. "But part Polish it must be, or you cannot have your American gifts for dinner."

"Part Polish? How can that be?" asked Anton.

"You will see," said Mrs. Pelaski firmly.

That evening the children were allowed to light the fat candle in the window and the string of gay electric lights on the little tree.

The gifts were to wait till the morrow. "And mind!" warned Mrs. Pelaski, "a Polish Christmas first—or no gifts." And Mr. Pelaski smiled at his wife, then nodded gravely at the children.

A Polish Christmas first! Whatever did Mother mean?

But Mother's word was law when she spoke that way. They knew that.

Very quietly the children came downstairs on Christmas morning. They were anxious, not knowing what to expect. They started back in surprise as they reached the dining room. The table was laid for breakfast, and at every plate were packages that set them wondering.

But the biggest surprise was Mother—Mother, who always wore a simple American frock in the morning, now arrayed in the strangest-looking costume. There was a gay waist with puffy sleeves—very beautiful, the children thought. But the strangest part was the skirt, so very full that it looked as though it had a hoop beneath. There were tucks in the skirt and many gathers.

When Mrs. Pelaski saw the children's astonishment, she laughed and told them to look at her dress very carefully. The skirt her mother had made for her when she was only seven years old. She had woven the cloth herself, had the mother, and it was very, very strong. Then she had tucked the skirt from the hem clear to the waist and had put as many gathers in as she possibly could before sewing it on the little band.

That was so that, as the little girl grew, a tuck or two could be let out each year as the skirt needed lengthening, and the gathers loosened as the belt was made larger.

Of course, new waists had to be made to the fine skirt, but

mother had worn the skirt for her best until she had come to America. "And see," she said proudly, "it is still as good as new. My mother wore her skirt for nearly forty years."

The children gasped in amazement.

"Is your dress the Polish part of our Christmas, Mother?" asked Marcelline.

"Only a part," answered her mother. "In Poland, before we had our Christmas feast, all the members of our family kissed one another on the cheek and forgave any wrongs done one to another, and also asked forgiveness from one another for right things they had failed to do."

As Mother looked at them gravely but lovingly, and Father waited to see what they would do, all the children dropped their eyes.

"I guess," said Moritz, the quickest of the children, "I shouldn't have called it an old Polish Christmas. I guess it was a very good kind of Christmas." He looked at his mother.

"Anything else, Moritz?" she asked gently.

Moritz hung his head. "Well, of course, I know Anton can play ball all right. I was jealous."

"Good, son," said Mr. Pelaski.

"I didn't mean to kick Ed," said Anton, as his mother looked at him. "I was just mad about my skates."

"I—I took 'em, Anton," said Edouard with a lump in his throat. "I'm sorry, and I'm sorry I pinched Clara."

"That's all right," said Anton sheepishly.

Mother looked at Marcelline. "I'm sorry I slapped Clara," said Marcelline in a low voice.

"And is our little Clara sorry she screamed and kicked?" asked Mrs. Pelaski.

"I won't, even if Ed pinches me again," promised Clara.

"Now," said Mother, "each one of you must kiss the rest on the cheek as a sign of forgiveness and love, and then we'll all have the right spirit for our Christmas feast."

The children looked a little shy. Moritz and Anton and Edouard hoped the other boys at school wouldn't find it out. They'd never seen American boys kiss each other. But there were the packages on the table. And there in the kitchen were the ducks all stuffed for roasting. Better get it over. Shamefacedly they went from one to another, each one implanting shy kisses on the cheeks of the rest.

And then everybody was happy. The lovely Polish custom had made their hearts ready for the best kind of American Christmas, one in which the Christ-child could be the unseen, welcome guest.

(THE SOUTH)

For the Children from Possum Run

GRACE NOLL CROWELL

THIS December day the big house, with its shutters closed behind its great, white-pillared porticoes, looked for all the world like a huge, sleeping giant. The magnolia trees on the lawn seemed to wrap it about with warm protectiveness, and the winter grass, lovingly tended by black hands, was a dazzling emerald, rich enough and big enough to blanket even the big house.

The front of the building was indeed silent and deserted, but in the back, the yard was electric with shock and excitement. Something was going to happen. Something wonderful!

Mose, the yardman, fairly clapped his heels in his going about. Old Ivory, his huge black wife, the cook for many years at the big house, was all ashake, and bitingly arrogant in her demands on Lilybelle, her son's erstwhile wife, and the mother of little bullet-headed Tobe. The son, Morgan Lindsey, named after Colonel Morgan Lindsey, owner of the big house and proprietor of the great plantation that stretched far away in the distance, had proved a disgrace to the name; but many a rascally namesake has managed to live in the shadow of glory and greatness, and remain unnoticed and unsung, and for the most part, unjailed, as had old Mose's boy.

"Yo' crack yo' heels, Lilybelle," Ivory flung out. "Get into that house an' give them beds a good airin', an' don't yo' dast look into things yo' no business lookin' into. Yo' har? Now git."

"Morgan Lindsey, ain't yo' wrung them chickens' necks yet? Reckon yo' so lazy even them spindly fryers is too big a job fo' yo'. Get goin', I tell yo'," and, "Mose, Mose," she shrieked, "yo' polish that silvah, an' don' leave no black—har me?" Turning to the turnip greens she was cleaning at the out-of-door trough, she addressed herself to them: "Yo' better git clean. Colonel Lindsey, he like his potlikker ungritted same as the next 'un." Then, strangely sweet after her tirade, her reedy voice lifted in song:

"'Yo' said if I be lifted up,
I'll be yo' fathah, I'll be yo'mothah,
I'll be yo' sistah, I'll be yo' brothah,
An' I'se gwine to lift yo' up.'"

Colonel J. Morgan Lindsey and his wife, "Miss Caroline," were coming home. For a year—a strange, terrible, feverish year—they had been gone from the big house. They had been running away from a great, overwhelming sorrow, and they found that it could not be done. Last year their little daughter, Caroline, had died as suddenly as a candle flame that is blown out by a quick strong wind. Their little, lovely, eager-hearted, eight-year-old Caroline, their only child, the only child they could ever have, had been there one moment and gone the next! Little Caroline, who loved surprises, who could scarcely wait for any happy coming event, had gone in a breath, leaving unopened the gaily wrapped, mysterious packages labeled for her and grouped at the foot of the great shining tree that Christmas morning. She had left the big house that her presence had lighted like southern sunshine, had left the great halls and rooms as empty as if there were no life left anywhere at all; and the father and mother, stricken wordless with sorrow and numbed with shock, knowing that it was God who had called their child into heaven and had closed the door, tried hard to be reconciled, to bear their sorrow as they should, knowing that all his ways are right and good. Yet in their wild grieving they turned to each other and said:

"We must get away—away from the emptiness of the house,

the rooms. We must! We must! We will travel far. We will fly on great planes. Perhaps the wind from the stars will blow the agony from our hearts. We will sail on great liners. It may be the waves will soothe us and give us rest and peace. We will not come back until—until we are able to bear the house, the rooms, to bear Christmas here . . ."

There is nothing more heartening to a weary Southern traveler than the welcome home of long-time faithful and trusted colored servants. Miss Caroline, dreading, in spite of her high resolve, to enter the house of tragic memories, fearful lest her new-found courage fail her, felt that warmth envelop her, and was humbly grateful for it. There was old Ivory, her arms widely outstretched, reaching out—not quite touching her—embracing her, as it were, in her own and only way. Her "Lor', Mis' Ca'oline, yo' sho' does look good to me! An' I'se sho' glad to see yo', too, Boss-Man!"; Lilybelle's simpering and Morgan Lindsey's stammering; even little bullet-headed Tobe's white-toothed grin from behind his mother's skirts—all were joyously welcoming.

"We decided to come home for Christmas, Ivory. We are going to open the house. We shall have a Christmas tree," Miss Caroline said bravely. "We felt that it would be better so."

"Sho' enough, Mis' Ca'oline? Is yo' sho' yo' kin do it?" Ivory's rolling eyes showed her astonishment. "Is yo' sho'?"

"Yes, Ivory, we are quite sure. Little Caroline came to me in a dream. She was beautiful—like golden light. She was like all the joy there is in the world. She spoke to me. She told me she is happy, that she wants us to be happy. She wanted us to come home, and so we came."

Ivory's eyes all but rolled from her head at this. A "ha'nt," no matter how greatly beloved the departed one might be, was too unearthly, too terrifying, for her nerves, deeply embedded though they were.

"And so we came home for Christmas. We are going to open the house. We shall have a tree," Miss Caroline continued. "We felt we should. That it would be best."

"Yo' all will ask all the city folks, Ah reckon?"

"No, Ivory. We aren't going to invite our old friends this

time. We shall begin very special preparations tomorrow. We want all the children from Possum Run to come to our Christmas party. Every one of them."

"Yo' doesn't mean it, Mis' Ca'oline, does yo'? Why, they'se jest po' white trash. Yo' all mean the Hill chilluns, isn't yo'? They'se Grade A. They'se really Grade A." Ivory had bottled too much milk to fail to know the significance of the letter.

"No, Ivory, we feel that little Caroline would like for us to go into the highways and the byways this time. Oh, Ivory, she is so beautifully, goldenly happy! She wants everyone to be happy. She said so. She spoke of other children . . ." And Miss Caroline closed her eyes a moment to recall more clearly the radiant vision. "She would like for us to do this thing we have planned. I know she would."

"Aw right, Mis' Ca'oline," Ivory hastened, wide-eyed and shivery at the thought of the heavenly apparition. "Mose'll go down tomorrow an' invite 'em. But I spect we won't git cleaned up all wintah once they been heah. They'se Grade B folks, an' mighty po' Grade B." And thus having unburdened herself, she waddled kitchenward, singing at the top of her voice:

> " 'Yes, the blessed Christ was bo'n,
> In a meek an' 'umble fo'm,
> To reach a wretched sinnah just like me,
> Had he come a hia'h way
> Then the rich would have their say,
> He's the joy o' my salvation, yes he is,
> Yes he is.' "

Early the next morning the great preparations began. Five days in which to accomplish the innumerable, all but impossible, tasks: the great tree to be cut in the woods and brought home to be decorated more brilliantly, more beautifully than any tree had ever been; the many gifts to be bought; cooking to be done until the huge kitchen range would glow and dance to keep up with it all; Ivory's black arms white to the elbows in flour; Mose, flapping about his tasks for all the world like the turkeys whose heads he would cut off.

Morgan Lindsey drove the great limousine to the nearby city, parking in front of dime stores or driving through the throngs while Miss Caroline shopped in the big stores. Little Tobe at his side, his eyes popping at the unusual sights, missed nothing of the city's gay excitement. He saw the Salvation Army lassies clanging their bells above the screened kettles that held the bright, tossed coins. He blinked at the city workers as they climbed the poles of the street lamps to finish their task of hanging the fragrant cedar wreaths, and the red and silver bells there for decoration. He even thought—yes, he did glimpse a red-robed figure—the huge bearded Santa Claus who roamed the streets ready and willing to lend a heavily swathed ear to little children's wants. This, indeed, was wonderland to little bullet-headed Tobe from the country. And there was Miss Caroline, coming home from her great tasks, tired enough to rest, to sleep the night through, a thing she had not been able to do through the past long year. Always she was sustained by the glory of what she had seen: little Caroline, glad and happy in her heavenly home, with Christmas more dazzlingly beautiful there than any on earth could be; little Caroline, wanting her father and mother to be happy, wanting them to forget a thing that was past, that no longer mattered because of the present radiance and the joys that are waiting in the eternal Christmases.

Mose had done his work with reluctance, but he had done it well. Who was he to be associating with white trash? he thought as he trudged from weathered shack to tumbledown shack in Possum Run. "How many chilluns yo' all got?" he would question disdainfully. "My Boss-Man say he wants fo' yo' all to let yo' young-uns come to a pahty at the big house, six o'clock Christmas Eve. He sho' does." Then on and on: "How many yo' all got? Five? An' yo'? An' yo'? magically storing the number away under his gray thatch of wool to be remembered later. And on he went, receiving stoical replies and laconic promises that all the children would come trudging across the fields to the big house on Christmas Eve. And they came. How they did come! Emmie Porgy, her tattered rags pinned together; Johnnie Cook, barefoot and unwashed; little Eve Parish, up from a recent illness, as pale as a jasmine bloom, yet with eyes like stars in her intense excitement; Andy Boles, on his crutches—Andy who had never walked quite right, and who seemed to be getting worse as the days went by; Mary Curry, her face shining from the harsh soap she had used, part of her black hair untangled by combing, part of it a wild snarl—these and many others: the children of the poor came to the big house. They were very shy at first, very ill at ease before the great people in the beautiful home. Their blinking eyes took in the wide halls, the sparkling crystal chandeliers, the laden table spread the length of the great high-ceilinged dining room.

Colonel J. Morgan Lindsey and Miss Caroline greeted their guests cordially, while the black faces of Mose and Ivory and little Tobe peered through a crack of the kitchen door, curious to note how the "po' white trash" behaved themselves on such an occasion.

Never before had the children seen such a magnificent feast: the turkeys brown on their platters; the sweet potatoes fluffed and frosted with marshmallows; the grits, golden with giblet gravy; the cranberries like rubies in their crystal bowls; and finally, the roasted pecans, gathered from the Lindsey pecan groves; the frozen delicious cream—cream from the great Jersey herds; and the cake that had been whipped to feathers by Ivory's black hands.

Then the tree, the peak of joy, flashed on their view as the great doors were flung open at last. Its brilliant beauty was enough to blind the strongest eyes: tinsel like rain in the sunlight; baubles that glittered with blue and crimson and gold lights from its frosted depths; a huge star teetering on its tip; countless firefly lights blinking through the branches at the dazzled and breathless children.

Colonel J. Morgan Lindsey himself distributed the gifts. It eased the hurt in his heart, some way, as he handed them out to these children of the poor—each child receiving all that his or her arms could hold. The big house had never before witnessed such unbounded joy. Mose and Ivory, peeping through the doors, were dumbfounded at the sight. At last Ivory found her tongue: "Ah spects Ah never will git cleaned up aftah them po' white trash, but they sho' does look shiny glad, an' Lor', Mose, the Big Boss-Man, an' Mis' Ca'oline, they looks glad too. Ah spect they had needed baptism like as fiah befo' they could come up about little Mis' Ca'oline, and this look like it is it."

After the wild excitement and joy of receiving the gifts, Miss Caroline suggested that the lights be turned out, and with only the firelight on the grate, and the glow from the great tree, she sat down at the piano, and the music of the old sweet carols rang through the rooms, Miss Caroline leading, and the children's voices, silent at first, then at Miss Caroline's insistence timidly lifting, some of them sweet and clear, some tuneless, but making up for it with great volume:

" 'O little town of Bethlehem,
How still we see thee lie;
Above thy deep and dreamless sleep
The silent stars go by.
Yet in thy dark streets shineth
The everlasting Light; . . .' "

Miss Caroline watched the children through a mist of tears, her heart yearning for her own child with an unutterable longing. Then again the radiant golden vision brought its assurance of happiness beyond any mortal dreaming. The golden light seemed to move, to fall like a halo about little Eve Parish, the pale child just up from a recent illness. The starry eyes caught and held Miss Caroline's until her fingers stumbled a bit over the keys. Little Eve, who needed mothering so, who needed food and clothing and medicine, who would be beautiful if she were loved and tended—who reminded her somewhat of little Caroline: the lovely blue of her eyes, her hair filled with honey-colored lights—the look of heaven about her . . .

They sang again:

" 'Silent night! holy night!
All is calm, all is bright,
Round yon Virgin Mother and Child! . . .' "

Always the mother for the child—the child for the mother! Miss Caroline could go no farther in her singing. The sudden urge to mother all the children of the earth was clamoring in her heart. A universal motherhood! Why could she not spend the rest of her life in work among the lowly? The little Christ-child was lowly. Would she not be serving him by serving these children clustered about her here? There was time and money—plenty of time, enough money. If she could know what to do—how to go about it. She would ask God; he would tell her. Perhaps she would be able to climb out of the dark valley of self-absorption and despair up to the golden hills of light through service. She might really be helpful to these children at her back door; might help them to higher and better living. If she only could! Then perhaps little Caroline's death would not be in vain—perhaps it was true that God does make all things work together for our good if we love him sincerely . . .

The lights were turned on again, and Colonel Lindsey suggested that they gather on the veranda to see the fireworks, so much a part of a Southern Christmas that the party would not have been complete without such a demonstration. Morgan Lindsey, pompous and important at his assigned task, was master of ceremonies, and the children, warmly wrapped against any possible winter chill, and carefully guarded from harm, watched the beautiful, breath-taking rockets climb the sky and burst in a shower of glory. They cried out at the loveliness of the gold and crimson and blue balls of the Roman candles that broke against the night in sudden blazing splendor. They shivered with delight over the huge sparklers sending their white stars upward, outward, in bouquets of brightness, and they gave little shrieks of laughter at the firecrackers' violent explosions, and at the fizzers that could not quite find the power to take their fiery way through the night.

Miss Caroline stepped quietly over beside little Eve Parish, who stood apart from the others.

"Honey," she asked, "where do you live?"

"T'other side of Possum Run, in the hollow by the creek," the child answered shyly.

"Have you any brothers and sisters, dear?"

"No, Ma'am. I live with my uncle and aunt and cousins. Lots of cousins. See, there's Jimmie an' Red an' Hettie an' Jeff an' Mattie," she pointed them out among the other children, "an' the baby's at home."

"I'm coming to see you soon," Miss Caroline said. "May I?"

"Oh, yes, Ma'am. I would like that." Her eyes were starrier than ever, but they grew suddenly troubled. Was not Miss Caroline the most beautiful person she had ever seen? Her eyes, her hands, her ways? But what would Uncle Joe and Aunt Het say? How would they behave? Perhaps they would be ugly and cross to Miss Caroline, the beautiful lady.

Tears sprang to the child's eyes. "I want yo' to come," she said, "but maybe yo' best not. Yo' see, my uncle and aunt—they—they don't always treat company so good."

"I will come anyway," Miss Caroline smiled. "I will come just to see you. Shall we say I will tomorrow?"

"Well'um." The little girl gave a half-glad, half-frightened assent. And so it came about that the next afternoon the great limousine from the big house stopped at the tumbledown gate of the Joe Hart home, and Morgan Lindsey, very proper and proud in his new Christmas livery, opened the car door for Miss Caroline to alight. Little Eve, who had been eagerly awaiting her coming, stood back from the broken windowpane, paler than usual with conflicting emotions.

"What she want here?" Aunt Het exclaimed, catching sight of the visitor from the window. "She never come befo'. What's she wantin' now?"

No one made reply, and Aunt Het herself opened the door. "What yo' want?" she asked, a barbed hostility in her voice. "We ain't got nothin' in common with such as yo'."

Old Joe Hart arose from his rickety chair. "She's right. We don't need ya. Ya ain't paid us no mind before last night. What's on ya mind?"

"Please," Miss Caroline pleaded, "may I come in, just for a minute? I want to talk to you about little Eve."

"What yo' want to say 'bout that pindlin' young-un? She's no good to yo' or us either, al'ays around sick an' whinin'."

"I came to ask if I might take her home with me. She is ill. She shows it. She needs food and care and medicine. I should be glad to take her and care for her as I would my own daughter, if you will allow me to do so."

A slyness had crept into Joe Hart's small, beady eyes. "So ya want my niece, do ya? What ya want her for? Maybe, now, if ya make it worth my while, I jest possibly might turn her over to ya, but not without. What ya offerin'?"

"I am not offering to buy little Eve as if she were your slave. I want to help her. I want to see her grow rosy-cheeked and well again." And Miss Caroline slipped to the child's side and put her arm lovingly about the shivering little figure.

"Well, ya ain't gittin' her . . . unless," Joe contemplated a moment, "unless maybe ya could git Colonel Lindsey to swap two or three of his mules fer her. They'd come in mighty handy for the gradin' work. How about a swap, Mis' Lindsey?" he leered.

"If you will sign a paper to that effect," Miss Caroline said sternly, "I think the exchange can be managed."

"Reckon so. We got too many kids anyhow. One less'll do no harm, I reckon."

Little Eve was suddenly transported with joy. The light of happiness was an aura about her, as she took her place beside Miss Caroline and rode home with her through the lovely Southern winter twilight, to fill the vacancy in the big house and in the hearts of the bereaved father and mother, and to become a beneficent influence in the lives of the darkies on the place. Then only did the stark horror fully lift from their superstitious hearts, for only the loyalty of the Southern Negro for their white folks had kept them on at the big house, so great was their fear of a "ha'nt."

Miss Caroline realized the difficulties that lay ahead of her, the gigantic task she had undertaken. There would be the breaking down of the proud, stubborn wills of the parents of the neighborhood children, for there are no prouder people in the world than the born Southerner. There would have to be improvements in the schools; education where there had been none before. There would be Andy, needing medical attention because of his lame hip; there would be all the other children with their various and endless needs; but surely if the Lord wanted a work done, he would direct that work, he would strengthen the laborer.

That night she knelt at her window facing the high, white, silent stars as she prayed for guidance, for wisdom, for strength for this strange universal motherhood that she had chosen to undertake, and surely little golden-hearted Caroline watched from the parapet of heaven, and was on tiptoe with gladness. Surely, He who had sent His only Son centuries ago to serve among the lowly, heard and answered her selfless prayer that starlit Christmas night.

(SOUTHERN MOUNTAINS)

One of the Least Ones

EDNA AND HOWARD HONG

JIMALEE HITCHED her stumpy little split-bottom chair closer to the fire, and without letting go of her poppet doll, kicked at a green chunk hissing its reluctance to burn.

"Quit your snubbin', Baby-child," she crooned to the bundle in her arms. "Hit's sobby wood, but hit'll ketch now and warm you. Thar! Thar! You jist take a nap o' sleep."

Jimalee's spare little body lurched into the jolting bounce with which a mountain mother rocks her child to sleep, and her soft, low voice ascended into the high, nasal pitch which mountain children learn so early from the singing of their elders. It was not a lullaby she sang to her corn-husk doll, but a plaintive ballad of love trampled underfoot. In the simple story of overwhelming emotions, yet incomprehensible to her, Jimalee voiced her own little-girl's longing for a surrounding, embracing love.

" 'If I had wings and I could fly, I would fly away to my false lover,' " she sang.

A bough of spruce pine flared up and brightened the glint of horse-chestnut brown in Jimalee's long braids.

"I reckon if I had wings, Baby-child," she whispered to her poppet, "I would fly up yonder and find my mammy."

The spruce-pine bough shriveled in the flame and dropped, a gray skeleton, into the gray ashes. Jimalee hugged her poppet doll closer.

"But—mebbee—mebbee Mammy ain't thar! Mebbe she's down below." Jimalee shivered. "The preacher man says hit's mighty hard to git up yonder. God's mighty peevish, and he mightn't hev let her in. Oh, Baby-child, I wish I knowed for sure! Whenever I go to them preachin' meetin's in the church house I git afeared. If you axe me, Baby-child, I think—"

Jimalee looked over her shoulder fearfully and then pressed her lips close to the dried husk wrapped in an old blanket.

A heavy step on the porch brought Jimalee to her feet in sudden terror, certain that the Lord God himself had come to take her to eternal torment. When she saw that it was only Shad and Paw home from the all-night fox hunt, her legs suddenly felt as if they were made of paper.

"Waal now, Leetle One," grinned friendly, pranking Shad, "you look plum tuckered out. Air you ailin'?"

Jimalee shook her head silently. Her eyes darted to her father's face. Next to God, she feared most her father. It was not that he was a mean beast of a man, like Bill Halloway down at the end of the holler. It was that he was such a say-nothing man, and his say-nothingness cast shadows into Jimalee's sensitive soul.

Jimalee watched her father's deep-set eyes under his black, floppy hat pass sentence on the fire.

"Go 'long and tote in some chips," he ordered, and his voice was neither sharp nor kind.

Jimalee turned quickly to pick up the chip basket, but not quickly enough to hide her sudden tears from Shad.

"Shucks, Leetle One," he laughed, "what air your eyes puddlin' fur? Pappy didn't mean no harm."

Jimalee fled from Shad's miscomprehension. How could she tell them of her fears and loneliness? How could she tell them of cowering in her bed at night, trembling when the baying of the hound dogs on the ridge told her how far away the hunters were, how alone she was? How could she tell them that the many hours she spent alone were filled with painful longing for her dead mother and with horrible nightmares of Judgment Day? Even less could she tell the men that although their return and everyday presence brought relief from tormenting visions, it did not bring an end to her heartache and emptiness.

Shad and Paw were sleepy and silent over their warmed-up biscuits, fried potatoes, and pork meat, and rose abruptly from the table to stumble to bed. Jimalee listened for the sound of the heavy clunk of their shoes on the floor and thought dismally of the lonely day before her while the men lay prone in slumber in the other room and the hound dogs sprawled wearily before the kitchen stove, dreaming fitfully of pungent fox trails on moonlit nights. Terrified, she thought of the lurid imaginings which flocked about her when her father and Shad withdrew in heavy sleep. It was a relief to hear Shad call drowsily.

"I most forgot, Leetle One, Granny Prue hollered out and sez for you to come holp her a bit today. She ain't bin so peart. I reckon you best give her a hand."

Jimalee did not need Shad's encouragement. It was fun to help Granny Prue. Granny was "womenfolk" and understood little girls. Granny talked an arm or leg off a person, and Jimalee craved talk. Moreover, Granny's house was beautifully papered with pages from magazines which her granddaughter sent her from the Outside, and Jimalee could stand and read wonderfully exciting things while she washed and wiped the dishes.

Granny Prue's cabin was way up where the creek turtle-tailed out into several little forks. Jimalee never seemed to be able to get there very fast. In the summer she stopped too often to marvel at the flint pebbles shining like silver in the creek bottom or to listen to the trickle of the little streamlet which ran into the creek over a poplar root. Today she forgot all her indoor fears, looking at the winter beauty of the great, tall trees and the stubby little trees and bushes, all of them silvery with hoarfrost.

Granny sat primly in her cherry rocker before the fire when Jimalee came in.

"I calculated Shad plumb forgot to tell you, but hit's no

never mind. Oh, set down and breathe a spell. Hit ain't the work as much as I'm wantin' to lay eyes on you. I ain't much account no more, but I git along, and I'm thankful for that. Take Mollie Scroggs, now. She's bin in a doleful way ever since you war a leetle bitty wee one—"

"Granny," interrupted Jimalee, "tell about me when I was a little bitty wee one."

"Waal, now, you were mighty puny, but pleasant as a flower. Your maw would hev bin a plumb fool over you, seein' as how she'd hed a string of boys afore you."

"Tell me about my mammy," begged Jimalee.

The cherry rocker creaked, the fire snapped, and the shrewd old grandmother filled the hill child's cup of loneliness to overflowing with dreams of mother love.

The exalted vision of Jimalee's mother which Granny could always conjure up before the little girl's eyes did not remain long. Again, as always, a menacing figure cast its shadow over it and finally eclipsed it. Jimalee shrank from the spectacle of God, towering and austere and looking too much like the burly preacher who shouted about hellfire and torment until his breath came in puffs and his heavy jowls were an ugly purple. It was always this way. God was forever driving her out of paradise, even as he had very likely driven out her mother, her beautiful, kind mother.

"Jimalee, what's ailin' you?" asked Granny. "Looks like to me you seen a ghost."

"I reckon I better git to workin'. You want I should scrub the floor, Granny?"

"Waal, now, hit ain't p'tikler," Granny began, but Jimalee was already out of the door and running down the path to the spring and the big iron kettle for heating water.

"Hit jist makes a body downhearted," sighed Granny. "No maw, no womenfolks, and that pinin' inside her!"

It did not take long for the water in the big black kettle to get hot over a fire of pine knots, and in no time at all Jimalee was scrubbing around Granny's cherry rocker and listening to her rescue memories from oblivion. When she had backed out into the other room, she could barely hear Granny's frail voice above the swish-swish of her old straw broom. Her thoughts no longer tagged along behind Granny's memories but went racing off into her own world of fears and fancies. She was greatly surprised when she bumped up against the farthest wall and found that she had scrubbed herself into a corner and had to wait for the boards to dry before she could get out. Only then did she remember that Granny's walls were covered with pages torn from magazines and that she had never read them here in the woodbox corner. Eagerly Jimalee scrunched over and began to read.

The water in the scrub pail grew cold. Granny's voice in the other room droned off into silence, and the cherry rocker ceased squeaking.

There was no clock to tell how long Granny slept or when she awoke, but when she did, it was to find Jimalee, wide-eyed and intent, waiting impatiently at her elbow.

"I declare, child, you give me a start!"

"Granny—" There was a strange note in Jimalee's voice. "Granny, hit reads out thar by the woodbox that Jesus he was a baby-child. Hit ain't true. Hit's jist a magazine story. God's Son never was a least one, was he?"

"Hesh, child!"

Granny's tongue hesitated between words of pious reproof and lively amazement, but the look in Jimalee's face forbade them.

"Yes, he war," she answered simply.

"Does hit say so in the Bible book the preacher man reads at Sunday meetin'?"

"Yes, it do, Jimalee. It do, it do! Thar yonder on the table hit lays. Bring hit to me."

Jimalee brought the shabby book and laid it on Granny's knees. Granny's trembling fingers turned the pages.

"Hit's in Luke. Find hit, Jimalee. My eyesight's failin' me."

"I—I cain't, Granny." Jimalee's small voice confessed her confusion and shame. "I never larned the Book. I allers thought thar was only hellfire in hit."

"Waal, now, you needn't to fidget so. Cain't say as I blame you, the way you've bin reared up. Cain't say as I blame you fur not knowin' 'bout the Christ-child neither. Christmas here in the mountains ain't much more'n a shootin' and prankin' time, and up thar in the church house the preacher don't mention Christmas 'cause hit don't start people to troublin' over their sins."

"Christmas?"

"That's when Jesus-child war born. Here 'tis. Luke tells hit. Read, Jimalee."

" 'And it came to pass in those days . . .' "

Jimalee read slowly, lingering over the words as one uncovers an incredible treasure, not wishing to overlook the most infinitesimal fragment. When she had finished she stood in a long, tranquilizing silence.

"Hit says God's Son was a little bitty baby-child, and his mammy wropt him up good," mused Jimalee dreamily.

"Hit do, Jimalee. Hit do say that."

"And then he was a lad of a boy?"

"So he war!"

"And then he growed up?"

"He did so!"

"And now he's up thar with God, his Pappy?"

"There ain't no doubt. The Lord be praised!"

Jimalee sighed, and the grim specters floated away.

"If God was a jowerin', bossin', ole hateful with a grudge against us," she conjectured simply, "he'd never let his Son sot foot down here. If he sent his baby-child, I calculate he must love least ones."

In Jimalee's heart a whispering refrain became a swelling chant. "God loves! God loves! God loves!"

Suddenly Jimalee felt a desire to be alone, to take this tremulous new experience into the outdoors, to pinch it and see if it were really true.

"I reckon I'd better git on," she announced abruptly.

"Looks like hit's fixin' to snow. Won't you stay the night?"

"I ain't sugar, nor salt, nor nobody's honey," laughed Jimalee.

Outside the new discovery became a tingling in her fingertips and toes. An urge to laugh, to skip, to jump, and to run, all at the same time, confused her so that she stopped and looked through the naked branches at the curve of sky overhead.

"Mammy up yonder," she whispered, "God's Son was a least one."

When two jennies with scraggy winter coats aligned themselves across her path, she threw her arms around their necks and cried into their ears, "God's Son was a least one! Do you hear? God's Son was a least one!"

There was no light in the little cabin low in the hollow, and Jimalee did not light one. Quietly, lest she awaken the still sleeping men, she built up the fire in the fireplace. As quietly she crept into her bed and watched the flames flicker on the strings of dried apples and red peppers hanging from pegs on the walls. A sudden toss of flame revealed her forgotten poppet still sitting in Jimalee's stumpy little split-bottom chair. Jimalee padded across the puncheon floor in her bare feet and carried her back to bed.

"Baby-child," she whispered, drawing close the poppet doll in its ragged blanket, "Baby-child, God's Son was a least one, and his mammy wropt him up good."

Like a warm and woolly blanket, Jimalee's new-found love surrounded and warmed her being. Securely she fell asleep in it as the firelight and shadows played on the walls and ceiling.

(SWEDISH-AMERICAN)

A Swedish Christmas on the Delaware

ELSIE SINGMASTER

CHRISTINA HELM, named for Sweden's young queen, opened her eyes very wide; then, seeing only darkness, she closed them tight. Four months ago, in lovely August weather, she had left Gothenburg, where she had been born, and had sailed for New Sweden in America. The name of the ship was the *Örn*, which means Eagle. The year was 1646. . . .

Every single morning for four months she had wakened with

a question in her mind, a question that had not yet passed her lips: "Would there be Christmas where she was going?" Of all days in the year, Christmas was to her the best. On Christmas Day there were church services—she could hear the singing and smell the sweet boughs of the evergreens above the windows. On Second Day Christmas there were presents, and the Christmas pudding, all sweet and spicy, and visiting and being visited. How could one live in a country where there was no Christmas?

The bed in which she lay was built against a wooden wall standing firmly on solid rock on Tinicum Island in the Delaware River. The island had been called Tenacong by the Indians to whom it had belonged, but the Swedish people called it Tinicum, which was their pronunciation of Tenacong. Steady as the bed was, it seemed to Christina to rock, flinging her now this way, now that. It seemed to speed through space and hit solid objects. These objects were really waves, which, however liquid they might look, were like rocks when the side of the ship hit them.

For four months Christina had been swung back and forth. When the arc was short, the ship was like a cradle. Then she played on deck with her doll or with the ship's family of cats. When in livelier mood, the ocean seemed to fancy that the ship was a swing, and Christina was proud of what the captain called her "sea legs." When the wind was very high, the ocean treated the ship as a sling, with Christina as the missile.

Then Christina stayed in her berth, which was a part of her father's. It was very comfortable to feel his strong body beside her at night. When the arc was longest and the waves were hardest, he put his arm round her; then, whether she slept or lay in a sort of unconsciousness from so much buffeting, she forgot the wind and the waves and the ice that began to form on the rigging early in December.

She did not ask her father the question which troubled her; he had enough sorrow and trouble without having to answer unnecessary questions. Besides, time would answer it. She did not wish to ask the captain of the *Örn;* he seemed, like her father, abstracted. She didn't wish to ask the sailors—they had enough to do to keep the ship on its proper course to New Sweden. Little by little she became certain that there would be no Christmas there. She began to doubt, as week followed week, whether the ship would reach New Sweden at all.

All the aunts and uncles and cousins had come to the Gothenburg wharf to bid them Godspeed. Their tears and their comments didn't help Christina and her father in the least.

"It's a small ship!" said Uncle Peter.

"Leave the child here, Andreas!" begged Aunt Martha. "Don't take her among savages!"

Father might have explained that the inhabitants of New Sweden were not all savages, that besides Swedish people there were Dutch people and a few English people, and that there was a church and a godly and learned minister, but he stated none of these facts. He turned and looked down at Christina. His hair was darker than her flaxen pigtails, but his eyes and the shape of his face were exactly like hers.

"Do you want to stay here, Tina?"

Christina looked in only one direction—not back at Gothenburg, pleasant in the sunshine; not forward at the ocean, blue, unending, lonely; nor at the sails which were being unfurled with loud flappings, but straight up into her father's eyes.

"I want to go with you, Father."

The cousin nearest Christina in age took her round the neck. "You won't have any Christmas," she wailed. "No candles! No Christmas pudding. No cattle will talk on Christmas night! There are no cattle there!"

"There are cattle there," contradicted a boy cousin. "The first settlers took cattle out with them. But no one ever heard the cattle talk on Christmas night or at any other time."

"They do talk," insisted the little girl. "Only it isn't safe for anyone to try to listen to them; he'd get horned if he did."

"There's a box tree there that smells like raw fish," said the boy. "There are serpents on land twelve ells long, and there are spiders in the river with tails half an ell long and made like three-edged swords. With these the hardest trees may be sawed down."

Now Christina's father took a hand, seeing her round eyes. "Fine!" he said, smiling. "If we can only catch a few of those spiders, we won't have to send home for saws."

Again Christina opened her eyes wide in the darkness. She had imagined the motion; her bed was not moving, it was perfectly still. The stillness made her a little sick.

"Where am I?" she thought. The question which came into her mind each morning was forgotten in another moment. "Where is my father?"

She reached out her hand—her father was not beside her. She reached out her hand on the other side—there was the wooden wall.

"We've stopped moving," she thought. "Am I on the bottom of the ocean?"

She felt the wall—there was something strange about it, it was dry, not like the wet wall of the ship. At last she was wide enough awake to realize that there was a covering over her eyes—she pulled it away. There was a ticking of straw under her; it, too, was dry and not wet with salt water. There was—it couldn't be a sheet under her chin! The curtains before the bed were parted a tiny bit; she put out her hand and parted them a little more.

She could see a hooded hearth built on a platform and a bright fire burning. She could see a tall, carved clock. She saw, extending from wall to wall near the ceiling, carved rods on which hung towels, gaily embroidered or ornamented with cutwork and crocheting.

"I'm at my Uncle Peter's in Gothenburg," she thought, terrified. "They have taken me back while I slept. Oh, where is my father?"

She sat up. She was wearing a clean, soft gown; she had had nothing that was clean on the ocean. Her long braids fell over her shoulders. She seized one in each hand. "I am I," she thought. "But where is my father?"

She parted the curtains s little more. There, under the leaded-glass window, was the table on which Uncle Peter did his beautiful carving which people were glad to buy. He had carved much of the woodwork in the church; Queen Christina had seen and admired his wooden statues—a famous man was Uncle Peter. But his lathe was missing from the end of the table, and instead of carving tools there were books and an inkstand!

"We've certainly been shipwrecked," thought Christina in despair. "My father is gone!" she cried.

A little girl was sitting in front of the fireplace—Christina must have been sleepy indeed not to have noticed her before. Eyes unaccustomed to Swedish children might have thought the little girl and Christina twins, but a Swede would have seen that they were very different, though both had blue eyes and two blond pigtails. The little girl wore a white blouse and over it a close-fitting bodice of red, and a blue skirt. She came toward the bed.

"Well, sleepyhead," she laughed, "are you awake at last?"

Christina sat staring. She did not dare to ask, "Where is my father?" She said, "Who are you?"

The little girl laughed again. "I'm Elsa Printz. My father's governor of New Sweden. I have four sisters and one brother. My oldest sister, Armegot, is married to John Papegoya. My other sisters' names are Catharina and Christina and Gunilla. Gunilla's not much more than a baby. Gustaf is my brother."

"Is this New Sweden?" asked Christina stupidly.

"It is. This is Tinicum Island." Elsa pointed through the window. "Over there's New Gothenburg, named for Gothenburg where you came from."

It seemed that Christina's throat would burst. "Oh, where is my father?" she cried.

"Your father's at church."

"At church!"

"Surely! Did you think we had no church?"

Christina breathed a long sigh.

"Are there savages here?"

"Lots of them," laughed Elsa.

"Are you afraid of them?"

"Afraid of them? Not I. Nobody's afraid of them. We're friends with them and, besides, we have guns and cannons. They bring us skins to wear and wild birds to eat and my mother knits caps for them. They laugh and say, 'Ho, ho, ho!' when she gives them their caps. I can say the names of their villages—

Coaquannock and Necoponacka and Moyamensing and Passyunk. Can you get up?"

Christina slid down to the floor. "Of course I can. But I feel very queer."

"So would I if I'd slept as long as you have. You've slept two days and two nights. Your father carried you from the ship. My mother bathed you, and you slept all the time. We had to wake you and feed you."

"You did!"

"Yes, we did. Here are clothes you're to put on. And you're to eat a bowl of porridge. I'm to get it for you."

Christina put on heavy muslin underclothes and a white blouse, then a black bodice and a red skirt. Elsa dipped porridge from a pot which hung over the fire. Although it was not made of the white flour to which Christina was accustomed, but of yellow flour, it nevertheless tasted delicious.

"That's Indian meal!" explained Elsa. "You don't have that in Sweden. Scrape your bowl."

"I have."

Elsa held out her hand. "We don't need coats to go to church; it's very near. Come on."

"Are you sure my father is there?" asked Christina, the tight band round her throat.

"Certainly he is."

When they opened the door the air seemed warm, not like cold Swedish air. Christina could not take in at once all that she saw. There was the gray river with the *Örn* at anchor. There were houses like Governor Printz's house, only not quite so imposing; there was a church with a bell in the belfry. Across the river lay a low shore with houses. There were trees which had lost their leaves and also tall evergreens such as there were at home. Why, there was a tall pole and tied on it a grain sheaf for the birds, just as she had been accustomed to see all her life!

"Come, come," said Elsa, and pulled her by the hand.

The ground beneath their feet was only lightly frozen, not hard as iron like the ground at home. She could see no snow anywhere—how strange at Christmas! Elsa hurried her past two houses and opened the church door.

The congregation was standing; a strong voice filled the room. Several persons turned their heads, among them a tall man dressed in woolen knee breeches and a leather jacket. He held out his hand and Christina let go Elsa's hand and ran up the aisle; she would have run even if it had been an audience with the queen. She stopped beside her father, her throat tight, tears running down her cheeks.

She saw an altar, not high and grand like the altar in the church at home, but an altar nonetheless, with the Bible open upon it and the communion cup standing beside the Bible, and two candles burning in silver sticks. She smelled spruce—why, there were boughs above the windows as at home! She saw the minister—Johann Campanius was his name, she remembered suddenly. He wore a black gown and white bands. The bands were broad like those on the gown of the minister at home and very white and clean.

She saw the captain and the sailors from the *Örn* and the new Swedish faces—men and women and little boys and girls, half of them smiling at her, but her eyes did not rest long upon them. At one side of the church stood strange men, their bodies almost bare, their cheeks painted. They were so near she could almost touch them.

The minister was speaking in Swedish. "Let us pray the Lord's Prayer." "Our Father," began Christina with all the others. Then, astonished by a queer chorus, she paused. The Swedes said "Our Father" in their tongue; a few Dutchmen and an Englishman and his wife said it in theirs. Mingled with these she heard a strange grunting. The Indians were praying. Did they too know "Our Father"? She might have laughed if she had known that they said, not "Give us this day our daily bread," but "Give us this day our corn and venison." The minister had taught them this prayer, probably the first Christian prayer used by the Indians.

"And now let us sing," continued Pastor Campanius. "Let us sing, 'Good news from heaven the angels bring.' "

" 'Good news from heaven,' " sang Swedes and Dutch and English together. The Indians remained silent during the singing, but at the end they made admiring sounds.

Christina's father's arm was around her; she was leaning as heavily against him as a very light person could lean. Beside her Elsa laughed, "Tomorrow we'll have the Christmas pudding and the presents."

"Happy Christmas!" said the pastor. The church filled with a loud clamor. "Happy Christmas! Happy Christmas!"

Christina breathed a long and happy sigh, as though she had escaped a great danger. Of course there was Christmas in New Sweden!